Number Eighteen ~ 2008-09

New Millennium
WRITINGS

Winner of a Golden Press Card Award for Excellence

Edited by Don Williams
who dedicates this issue

To
Rebekah McCarroll
Who Shines

Don Williams, Editor
Contributing Editors for Poetry: *Laura Still and Doris Ivie*
For Prose: *David Hunter, Jon Manchip White & Allen Wier*

Assistant Editors: *Jeanne Tredup, Alexis Williams, Sarah Mate,
Lawrence Duby, David Joyner, Ouida Williams, Everette Bach,
Will Rickenbach, Nancy Rickenbach and Pamela Strickland*

Cover Art, 'Autumn Nocturne,' by Mark Sieger

Cover Design by *Rhonda Swicegood of Hart Graphics*
Typesetting & Layout by *Don Williams*

Special Thanks to
*The Tredup family of Kenosha, WI, John and Margie Richardson
and Travis, Justin, Rodney, Rebecca, Tim and Kathleen*

Website by *Mark Plemmons*
Visit the *NMW* Web page at **www.newmillenniumwritings.com**
or **www.writingawards.com**

Booksellers may purchase *NMW* **by contacting:**
New Messenger Books at 865-428-0389
PO Box 2463, Knoxville, TN 37901
DonWilliams7@charter.net

ISSN 1086-7678, ISBN 1-888338-25-3, CPDA BIPAD No. 89927

New Millennium Writings is published annually. Additional copies may
be purchased online at **www.newmillenniumwritings.com**, or send $12
check to *NMW*, **PO Box 2463, Knoxville, TN 37901**. For rules of the
twice-annual *NMW* Writing **Awards** for Fiction, Poetry and Nonfiction,
visit **www.writingawards.com**, or address envelopes to "Awards." Include a self-addressed, stamped business-size envelope. *NMW* does not
accept unsolicited poetry, fiction or nonfiction, except for entries in the
twice-annual *NMW* Awards or except for **interviews, profiles and trib-
utes to famous writers, living and dead** (for which we pay $100, plus
copies, if published). **Include sufficient SASE postage** if you want material returned, or letter-size SASE or email address for response only.

ℂontents ~ Featured Writers

Kurt Vonnegut on the Banks of the Big Tennessee, *139*

Maybe checking out on April 11, '07, at age 84 was lucky deliverance from times too much like those in a favored book—*1984* by George Orwell—or from a body and mind grown weary of medicinal hocus pocus. Either way, if Vonnegut and Faulkner are right to suggest the past is always with us, then Kurt still walks the banks of the Tennessee River as a young grad student and ponders doomsday weapons like those created in nearby Oak Ridge. ~ ***Read our Janus File tribute by Don Williams***

Photo by Jill Krementz

~ Poetry Suite continued next page

New Millennium Writings

Is pleased to present the New Millennium

Short-Short Fiction Awards

Winning entries appear on pages 6-25 (see Contents pages)

Summer 2007

Adrienne Pond, Austin, TX, *No Longer Strangers*
Louise Aronson, San Francisco, CA, *After*

Winter 2007-08

Susan Chiavelli, Santa Barbara, CA, *Winter Oranges*

HONORABLE MENTIONS

Summer 2007	*Winter 2007-08*
Cynthia Adams, Westminster, MD	David Anderson, Wellington, NV
Eve Brown, Deerfield, MA	Elizabeth Aquino, Los Angeles, CA
Mark Benedict, Waterford, MI	Nina Bayer, Bothell, WA
Paula C. Brancato, New York, NY	Al Burrelli, East Moriches, NY
Douglas Campbell, Pt. Marion, PA	Richard Cambridge, Cambridge, MA
Vincent Carella, San Rafael, CA	Karen M. Folger, Fort Collins, CO
Sarah Coury, Marshall, MI	Joyce Fox, Boca Raton, FL
Lisa Rae Cunningham, Atlanta, GA	Norton Girault, Norfolk,VA
Jenny Gumpertz, Palm Desert,CA	Enid Harlow, New York, NY
Eli Hastings, Seattle, WA	Chuck Kensler, Sebastopo, CA
Lisa Lenzo, Fennville, MI	Joe Kilgore, Chicago, IL
Peter L. Levy, San Francisco, CA	Mal King, Santa Paula, CA
Del Marbrook, Germantown, NY	Theora Joan Pleines, Fedhaven, FL
Ron Naples, Washington, IL	Donna Rubio, Marysville, MI
Veronica Patterson, Loveland, CO	Shari T. Smith, Newfane, VT
Jennifer Sears, Brooklyn, NY	David H. Snell, Paris, KY
Louise Farmer Smith, Wash., D.C.	E. Peregrine Til, Jonesboro, AR
John Taylor, Oak Park, IL	Sean M. Toren, Minneapolis, MN
Robert Thurber, N. Attleboro, MA	Juliet Wittman, Boulder, CO
Mikell Zacharia, Port Jervis, NY	Barbara Zimmermann, Yorktown, IN

For guidelines to our next contest, see page 9

Susan Chiavelli
Winter Oranges

*R*ain drips from a sky as gray as your father's wool sweater. It's the day before Christmas and you haven't seen the sun since late September.

The reading lamp is on even though it's only mid-afternoon. You live for the Mickey Mouse Club after school—for those glimpses of California and the magical kingdom that have melded into one mythic place. Your aunt, the one everyone says you look exactly like, lives in the *Golden State*. At least that's what she calls it in her letters. And you dream of going there someday, even though Mom says forget it. She already went once, to Hollywood before you were born, so she doesn't need to go again. Whenever there's talk of visiting California you look at your father's hopeful face, to see if maybe he'll say what you're wishing for. But he doesn't.

The tinsel covered tree shimmers in front of the big picture window on Christmas Eve. Your mother showed you and your sister how to put each strand of tinsel on, one by one. She says that's the only way to do it. You're not supposed to throw it on in clumps. It's supposed to look like icicles, not an explosion. But you think it looks like rain.

Your father put the lights on first—lights the size of walnuts and of every single color, even blue and orange ones, which are not really Christmasy at all, but more like California colors that somehow look out of place in your living room.

On Christmas Eve you eat the holiday dinner: roast beef (well done), potatoes, peas, and fruit salad with whipping cream dotted with maraschino cherries. Mom makes just enough for everyone to have exactly one helping. She doesn't like leftovers. There's always custard for dessert, for Dad's ulcers. But you and your sister can eat it too.

'Our stories are time capsules that contain what is otherwise destined to vanish—the essence of ourselves, our time, and place. I have a keen interest in telling stories from the view points of girls and young women, who are often marginalized or silenced. It is the exploration of the unsaid that illuminates the emotional truth we seek in any age.'

~ **Susan Chiavelli**

After dinner your family opens their presents, and you notice how you can watch everyone in the living room window against the shiny black night. It's like watching yourself in an episode of Twilight Zone where there are two parallel families, two trees, and twice as many gifts.

It's not a secret that you and your sister have been wishing for music boxes, the kind with pop-up ballerinas. Actually you want dancing lessons, but you know that's not possible, so you'll settle for watching a plastic ballerina dance.

One of your gifts *is* a round blue music box and your hand trembles when you open the lid. Tinkling music greets you—wish upon a star music—but there's nothing inside but an empty space. You turn it upside down looking for a secret button and when you can't find one, you ask where the ballerina is.

Your mother says they didn't have that kind at Sears. She says it's hard to please an ungrateful child. She opens the pink bubble bath you gave her, says she already has a lot of bubble bath.

Finally, Dad cuts the string on the brown paper package that came all the way from your aunt in Santa Barbara—the mystery box you've examined daily since it arrived—imagining all the possible gifts tucked inside: a map with a red-inked line marking the way to her house? Maybe even tickets to Disneyland? You hold your breath as he tears off the paper and makes a big production of opening the lid. Ta Da! The box is full of perfect oranges. Citrus scents the air and Dad smiles, but Mom sighs. She looks as if someone has sent her dirt.

"I don't like food as gifts," she says, twirling her bracelet as she admires the newest charm Dad gave her, a tiny golden bird. Mom looks at herself in the window, pats her long blonde pageboy into place. "There's nothing lasting about it."

Dad laughs at her, the same way he laughs at you when you won't eat your vegetables. "These aren't just *any* oranges," he says. His bear-paw hands reach into the box and he takes one out. He holds it up high in the palm of his hand—as if he's plucked a miniature sun from the sky.

"This grew on *my* sister's tree," he says. "Imagine." He raises the fruit to his face and inhales the scent. "She just walks out her back door and picks an orange for breakfast—in the *middle of winter.*"

Dad offers the fruit to Mom, but she refuses to take it. She folds her arms and hugs herself tight. When she's like that nothing will change her mind. Dad's smile fades, and suddenly your hand reaches out, but he closes his and makes the orange disappear. Then his hand opens slowly, like a flower, and he offers it to you. You take the orange from him, and you breathe in the aroma, exactly the way he did—all the while watching your mother's face. She gets up from her chair and looks at you as if she doesn't know who you are.

The music box stops playing. Your family's caught in the picture window—between your living room and the slippery black night—your sister trying on her new rubber boots, Mom turning away as she leaves the room, and Dad looking outside as raindrops slide down his face.

You move next to him and sit close by—so close that you can't tell in the reflection where he ends and you begin. You and your father peel your oranges together in silence, slowly, your fingers getting sticky with desire. The first bite is the sweetest, and without even knowing it you let the taste mingle with your dreams of California, until you've eaten each slice of the whole, until your dream is something lasting.

Adrienne Pond
No Longer Strangers

*T*he road to lure is the road of song as he subma-
rines his way through the penumbras of quarter
moon nights, dripping heated pitch down his sung-out
throat.

He is patience in faded jeans permanently soiled by dark earth
where warm air is breathed upon the skin of timber at dawn and long
walking leads to a woman; an early morning woman with auburn hair
the length of his arm and coffee temperatured above the inside of her
mouth. She wears thin lavender, silk and slit to thigh, smells of
crushed opium and her lips tremble every time she takes a drink.

He does not know her name, yet he waits daily to be ambushed by
her predictable presence. He thinks her sandals are too small and the
missing straps beg eroding conquistador-built roads to unbalance her.
Irretrievably drunk on her wobbling, sounds from the street trail off in
the corrosive greens that fall from the peripheries of weathered statues.

In the alley, there are pomegranates and men with violins and
dehydrated love looking for a place to live.

Today, it is the same sun as yestermorn, inciting competition of
shadows between weighted clouds and weighted buildings. *I decide*, it
says. *I will always decide.*

With sketchpad and charcoal, she squats amid light and silhouette
aside molded sculptures that would move inside her lower half if they
could. Her position extends the lavender slit, and caped carabinieri
forget to tell her not to touch places on bronze where four hundred
years of rain have searched for a missed crevice to lave. Her paper is
textured to resemble Pompeii frescos steamed off in layers, and the
first of her marks go down with sorrow at the thought of having taken
someone else's story to feed her own.

'My favorite writers are mavericks who can foreshadow a dare we must offer ourselves—to be better. They risk their lives, risk losing their jobs, risk losing love or have already been risked by someone else. Their words keep us from fleeing when all a morning may offer is cold stale fear of what next could crush the only edge left on a last dream. Writers are everyone's witnesses, reminding that last dreams can mutate and multiply into anything.'

~ Adrienne Pond

The man peels blackly hued grapes between his teeth and parlance, and October suggests coolly sharpened air is less painful than specific appetite. He tells himself that if strung instruments can imagine love in alleyways as rainfall begins in the backcountry and ends in the valley, then two strangers can imagine love in faded jeans and strapless sandals.

But what will happen when they are no longer strangers?

In walking, the early morning woman buys a mellow pomegranate, opens it with her mouth, and places the largest half in the man's exposed and anxious palm, without pausing, without speaking. As though she has just saved him from abstention. He chokes on bubbled silence rising from his lungs and does not recover in time. In shaded daydreaming, he imagines she slows her pace as he places pulp on her tongue and tells her enough.

In waiting hours he is handsomely vulnerable, aching for immense skies dusted with the ends of stars and the mouths of hope. In this acreage, his needs for one day could be met with the deeply lit falling of an ocher night, and carnivorous dreams of her. Not above begging for parchment and pen, he would set sorrow's topography to music long enough to surpass the world's compulsions to forget. He fools himself, though, for he would move to the island of Procida if it would erase his need for the early morning woman—the memory of her scent and her sex falling into cracked stone where vapid northern digits of mist that know nothing of love will carry them to the sweet graveless sea bottom. But he would not stop looking for her, even after Procida; it is the truth. Lace and land beneath oceans and sinking cities aside, not even Atlantis could cure him. It is also near to fact that while planning his escape he penned prose long enough to define a road for her and somehow 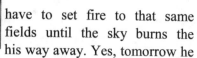 believed she would take it and decide for them both.

He thinks he will have to set fire to that same prose in grasses and fields until the sky burns the colors of war and lights his way away. Yes, tomorrow he will be gone from walks and a woman's pomegranate carmine tongue so love can never rehydrate in him.

In the repercussions of his leaving, when clouds surround buildings and together they prevent the casting of shadows, cicadas will not know to end their songs begun in darkness. In piles of fallen autumn leaves of fading siennas and mahoganies degrading in sand and sediment, before the dreams of children cease, the landscape will play ghostly echoes of anonymous midnight conversations among musicians and will satiate its own needs for sapphire rain and a woman and a speechless man with a descending fog.

Publishers of prose and layers of brick will toast their commonality, as if he'd already lined a path with his words and held fire in his other palm. He is beyond minor years, but he dreamed of writing as a child, trading games for graphite and gulping lyrics aside remnants of the shattered lives around him. Now, he dreams of olive trunks swallowed whole by Mediterranean vipers content in their feed and heaviness and impending drowning inside a flood the early morning woman brings.

Tomorrow, he will wear a suit and disguise himself from roaming desiccated love, using diction from the south to convince himself he is no poet and there are no roads save the one he is on. Sometime that day her drawing pad will perish in saturating rainwater. Lemon trees will bear fresh in far off acacia-bordered orchards of Sorrento.

Not so slowly, his verbiage will betray him and his suit will smolder in the protests of fire held hostage. With swelling winds and traveling smoke, he will have to change his clothes before he can change his mind. He wishes to change his mind.

When he finds her, she will be barefoot beside her drenched drawings on a road hedged with qualities for the taking. She will become the late evening woman. He will tell her he tried to leave but his clothing burned and all that remained were his writings.

Louise Aronson
After

*A*t the Rock Creek State Veterans Home where some people come and go but most come and stay, Rodney Brown, a.k.a. A-Rod, nudges the bible off the edge of his bed. It hits the floor with a slam and across the room K.C.'s eyes open, scan, then roll up, and he says, "Shit, man, not again. What the fuck time is it anyway?"

Rodney ignores K.C. and turns on his call light by slapping his left arm against the pressure-sensitive pad beside him on the bed. And then he waits, something he's getting good at, not that he has much choice, though at least he's better off than Danny Stockton who took one in the head or Pablo Villela who lives three floors up on the ward where you don't have to do anything for yourself, not even eat, not even breath.

He listens for footsteps. Sometimes he can tell which girl is coming by the way her shoes touch down on the linoleum: Zeny does a tap-shush, Carina makes a squeak-sigh-squeak, and big Grace—full of self-importance—sounds as solid and steady as a man. With Rita, his favorite, there's only the nearly inaudible brush of one nylon thigh against the other.

Unfortunately, Rodney's nose also works well—too well—and now it's telling him that someone somewhere not far enough away is crapping himself. He hopes it's K.C. and not him since the hall is completely quiet, meaning it's still the night shift, the staff sacked out in an empty bed or in the med room or wherever the hell else they hid when you needed them most.

Hallway light bleeds through gaps above and beneath the door then diffuses across the room. It's just bright enough that Rodney can see K. C.'s open eyes trained on that place where—for a few months—there'd been a *before* photo, K.C.'s arms around the woman who'd visited daily until the afternoon she didn't pull up the orange vinyl chair but stood to one side of K.C.'s bed and announced that she loved him but she was too young for all this, that she needed a life, a real life like the one she'd always dreamed of, and that she wished him well, and he'd always be in her prayers, and finally, that she really, really hoped they could be friends forever, no matter what.

Footsteps sound in the corridor. Rodney listens then smiles. It's Grace for sure, and he's about to advise K.C. to turn his head and catch some of the eye candy as big Gracey bows and reaches for the bible on the floor when out of the blue he gets a pain in his right foot, a sudden explosive burn like a lighter held to his toes.

"Oh fuck!" he yells, though the pain fades as quickly as it appeared, replaced by a smolder with a throbbing behind it.

K.C. asks if he's OK, but Rodney doesn't answer. He's concentrating, relaxing into a hurt so familiar it's almost as if he can smell the strange German pizza a nurse named Eva used to sneak him at the hospital in Landstuhl in those last, best days before they transferred him here. "You're lucky," she had whispered, placing tiny rounds of sausage and melted cheese on his tongue and jerking her chin at the other beds. Her breath, warm and sharp from cigarettes and coffee, traveled into his ear and down his torso, landing between his hips where it blossomed into a problem he could no longer solve.

Rodney blinks and drags his left wrist across his eyes; the pain's better now, no more than an ember. He looks down the bed at the bump that is his feet, a short, sloped ridge that might be anyone's feet or even part of the bed itself, and there's no movement down there, but that doesn't matter because this time he knows he felt something.

"Grace," he shouts, wondering where she went. He slaps the call light again, slaps it and slaps it. "Yo," he says to K.C. "Help me, man," but K.C. only grunts and pulls his pillow over his head.

Twenty minutes later—long enough for Rodney to be certain it's all coming back: the toe, the foot, the leg, everything—he hears the solid, steady steps again.

"Hey," he calls, "Gracey, please," and the door opens.

The person in the doorway isn't Grace or any of the other girls but a guy Rodney's never seen before, a guy who would have been a total

'Every day, the media announces the latest number of dead American serviceper- sons as if that figure is the best and most accu- rate benchmark of war-related losses. I wrote this story to offer a small glimpse of the larger and far more disturb- ing picture, in which both death and the American experience of the war are just fractions of the whole.'

~ **Louise Aronson**

waste of his time earlier, since he would never, ever, watch some Joe bend no matter how hard up he was. In fact, he decides, he won't even mention the fallen bible to the guy, he'll just call again later, hoping for Zeny with her small, soft fingers or Rita with her high-riding ass. But the guy can help him with something more important than a quickie thrill, more important—at least for this one moment—than even the good book itself, and so he says, "My right foot, man! I feel it!"

The aide nods and pulls back the covers, and together they stare at the white space on the sheet next to Rodney's left leg. And Rodney closes his eyes and waves the aide away.

Every morning he somehow forgets. Every morning he wakes up and recognizes the hospital bed and the colorless walls he shares with K.C., and he remembers he's damaged but he forgets precisely how or why, and for a while—seconds at least, but sometimes much, much longer—he imagines that it's not really so bad, that what's left of him was worth saving. But then he remembers, and the remembering changes everything.

Sarah Coury
Kathleen Maria

I *named her Kathleen Maria, my little white pod. Small as a cat's eye, she had come months too soon. She was born in a cinema restroom, as next door Neo handed Agent Smith his own ass on a platter, and the crowd's many faces glowed in the affirmation: Goodness is the strongest force, it's just that simple.*

Kathleen Maria lit a fire from my ribs to my knees. She came like some holy cocoon on the tip of a spear, pale as a pearl in a scarlet puddle, a soul who would float in potential forever. A tiny vibrating beauty.

My purse contained an art nouveau matchbox which had been with me for years. Engraved on its top, a young stag turned his head away slightly, as a torrent of grapevines and lilies offered him up. I dumped out the matches and put Kathleen Maria inside.

My incredulous date drove me home. I threw my clothes away and slept for fourteen hours.

I walked in the dawn, the town sleeping shyly, to bury my box of this vague beloved stranger. Drowsy fingers felt around for my back pocket flask, a comfort motion which even the sweet chattering of maternity had never discouraged.

I reached the banks of Lake Superior, clear and cold and haunting as liquid moons, and walked inside. When the water reached my chest I swam, swam to water deep enough to hide a shipwreck. My matchbox, my Kathleen and I together slid beneath the waves. Here

'The writing process gives the perfect opportunity to dump a human heart out on the desk like a shoe box found in the attic, and take inventory of the scraps and trinkets inside. The joy for me is in trying to describe these contents in a way that does them justice, with honesty and reverence. Luckily, the written word can be as versatile as our natures, at once brutal and vulnerable, vulgar and sublime. A story for entertainment alone is wonderful, but I think its greatest potential is reached when the things we don't speak of are explored.'

~ Sarah Coury

lay all quietude which had seeped out of the land; the very idea of death and rebirth could have sprung from this place. I imagined I heard you begin to stir, begin to hum within your dainty vessel. It tumbled from my hand like an acrobat toward deeper silent sands. A slender stag in a tangle of flora guards you, turning his head for eternity toward you.

I walked home with daylight growing in my eyes, motors and murmurs and charity bells wakening. Along the road, the birches swayed like a thousand happy hags above, using words I could not discern to propel me down their blazing trail. I will continue mining pardon's breast from a paralyzed state of lilies, from a suitcase full of vodka, from the singing wrens, that I may be some subtle design of mother to you yet. Perhaps you might be held among the particles of air, in the moments of a dream when one could swear "I've known this girl before..."

And though I cannot see the form which I describe, I know that it is shining. In a sun which is elsewhere.

Eve Brown
Losing Africa

"**I** want to embrace my inner black woman," she said. The white woman loosened the kitenge wrapped around her ample waist and sat down. The rest of the women sitting around the circle stared as she kicked off her rubber flip flops, revealing ornate designs hennaed onto her calloused, pink feet. "I thought being part of this group would help me keep my ties to Africa."

"What the fuck kind of craziness is this?" Dionne demanded through her teeth. "This is a Women of Color group. You can see that. You, Bwahaha," she said jabbing her finger, "or whatever you call yourself, cause I know that ain't the name your mama gave you, you most certainly do not belong here." The other women sized her up, taking in how the light practically shone right through her skin.

"Bwahinmaa," the white woman said, making the word roll elegantly off her tongue. "It's the name I was given in Africa."

"Africa, my ass!" Dionne stood and took a step toward the woman. "You're just another white woman looking for culture! And anybody's culture will do."

"Now, wait a minute," Kim interrupted. "Everyone is entitled to self-identify and self-select. No one had the right to tell us whether or not we could come to these meetings. So Bwa ..." she hesitated. "She has the right to decide that she belongs in this group if she wants."

"Yeah, well, she has the right to decide. But you don't just decide that you are a woman of color. No, baby. That shit gets decided for you. It was decided for me the day your people dragged my people out of Africa."

'It helps to have talent. But I believe what really helps you succeed is how hard you'll work and how many times you'll hear no and still not give up. It took me more than thirteen years to get my first book published. But it was worth every minute of hard work and perseverance.

'After living in Ecuador for a year, I felt partially Ecuadorian. And after living in Uganda for three years, literally getting caught up in their civil war and having a baby there, well, I felt more than a little bit Ugandan. In this story, I wanted to explore the experience of being seen as "white," yet feeling "other."'

~ **Eve Brown**

"You don't know a thing about me or *my people.*"

"Yeah, well, I know color and you ain't no woman of color."

Kim held up her hand. "Whoa, let's all take a deep breath, here." She looked over at the white woman. "Bwa... *what's* your name?"

"Bwahinmaa. It means one who has left her community."

"That's nice. Is that the name they gave you when you got to Africa?"

"No, they called me *Tubab* for the longest time," she laughed. "That means white stranger."

"That shit's right," another woman said under her breath.

"Bwahinmaa was the name they gave me when I left Africa."

"Yeah, that's real sweet," Dionne raised her voice. "But we can't have no lily-white sisters in here. That's not the point."

"Just chill, Dionne," Kim said. "Bwahinmaa, could you give the group some time to discuss this? Why don't you wait out in the hallway. We'll come get you in a few minutes."

She rose gracefully and retied her *kitenge* in one fluid motion, picked up her woven bag and walked out of the room. In the hallway, she felt the heat in her face and collapsed into a chair. She could hear their voices coming from the other side of the door and she hated those women. She hated them: wrapped in *kinte* cloth and knowing nothing about the bony fingers that wove it. Crying for the lost tit of milk and honey yanked from their mouths, but never tasting its bitterness. Certain they'd all be queens right now if only their ancestors had not been dragged to America.

She shook her head and closed her eyes and could see the women of her village. Their black skin matted gray from dust as they coaxed water out of a dry well. Their long, tired breasts flapping dully as they pounded cassava into the tasteless meal that they prepared day after day. She could see them with their babies tied to their backs, babies with scrawny arms and distended bellies. She could see their children, too resigned to shoo the flies out of their eyes, their noses, their ears.

"Ha," she said out loud as she looked at the closed door. "What the hell do you know about Africa?" *I was the one who lived on what we could scratch out of that damn anorexic soil,* she thought. *I was the one who danced with the children under the full moon. I was the one who keened and wailed when they banged the funeral drums. How dare you judge me!*

How could they possibly know that, like them, she looked for the black faces on the streets, longed for them? And if she stared too long it was only because she was trying to recognize someone familiar.

"I was the one they called 'Mama Aisha,'" she yelled at the door.

They say that babies begin to recognize themselves by looking at those around them. She remembered the day Aisha realized she had a nose because Mama had a nose. She had a mouth because Mama had a mouth. For all the years she lived in that scabby village in Burkina Faso she had not looked in a mirror, and in her mind she looked just like everyone around her. After awhile even her neighbors seemed to forget about her color.

She had once read that the human body constantly regenerates itself—sloughing off old cells and creating new ones every day. So, after four years in Africa, wasn't she part African?

"I was the one who threw in the first handful of dirt on the day we buried my daughter. In Africa," she hissed at the door. "So don't tell me I am not an African woman. I have *lost* more of Africa than you will ever have."

When they opened the door to invite her back in, she was gone.

Jenny Gumpertz
Peeling Onions

*N*ews item: *A housewife has been arrested for stabbing her husband to death, which she claims was accidental. The husband came into the kitchen while she was peeling onions, and he fell onto her knife, which penetrated 5 inches into his chest. Neighbors were alerted to the tragedy by the yowling of the family cat. When the police arrived, the wife's mother was brewing tea to comfort her daughter.*

*

The wife's tale: I was in the kitchen peeling onions. They stung my eyes, and perhaps I was crying. I heard my dear husband run into the room and turned with the knife in my hand. He had an angry look on his face, the reason for which I do not know. He started toward me and seemed to throw himself onto my knife. I was holding it firmly, the reason for which I do not know. Perhaps I always hold my knife in this fashion. Perhaps I was startled by his suddenly confronting me this way.

*

Her mother's tale: My daughter is blameless. It is a clear case of self-defense. My son-in-law was a brutal man. He would get drunk and beat my daughter every night before taking her off to bed. I heard them, I heard it all. The night in question, he rushed into the kitchen in a drunken rage and she defended herself with the knife in her hand. She had been peeling onions. Now he is dead, and good riddance.

*

The ghost's tale: I was in my living room after a hard day's work making money for my lazy wife and her sharp-tongued mother who lives

21

'For me, writing is an exploration, a slog through the jungle with notebook and camera but no quarry in sight, till finally I stumble into a clearing where my characters are tenting for the night, sitting around the campfire toasting marshmallows and telling their stories.
"Peeling Onions" was a relatively short slog. It grew out of a news report similar to the one quoted in the story. The report puzzled me, and this is my explanation for the events. My credo: work hard, stay open, be of good cheer.'

~ Jenny Gumpertz

with us. I poured myself a drink of whiskey and was starting to read the newspaper when I heard my wife crying over her lover. This has been a cause of shame and distress to me—how can she think I can endure her keeping a lover? I went into the kitchen to tell her to shut up her crying, and she turned toward me with her knife pointed. But her tears made me sad and I went to put my arms around her. She leaped forward and plunged the knife into my heart. Now I am dead, and all because she had a lover and I felt sorry for her. I should have punished her instead.

*

The cat's tale: Some of what you have heard is true, and the rest is bunk. My mistress was preparing a delicious stew of beef and vegetables for my master's dinner and was crying over her onions. My master is a brutal man and often beats her, but she foolishly loves him. The mother-in-law is an eavesdropper and troublemaker but has nothing to do with this story. That night, when my drunken master ran into the kitchen with a rageful look on his face, my mistress turned in surprise. Seeing a knife in her hand, my master became even more enraged and ran toward her. He fell onto the knife because he had stepped on my tail. I was injured as well, and no one has offered me sympathy.

*

Her lover's tale: Please leave me out of this, I have not yet entered the picture. But after I do, I shall marry her. I shall take her away from that house and move to another city, and she can cook her delicious stew for me. There will be no mother-in-law to overhear our lovemaking, and if we have a cat, I will cut off its tail.

Short-Short Fiction

Barbara Zimmermann
Manhattans Imperfect

My laughter makes my sister cry. Doubling over and clutching my sleeve, she chokes and sputters, "Oh, Bobbie, bless you." Each time, I wait until Kate has sat upright and settled into a mild sniff and snort before asking why my cracking up grieves her. She never answers directly, instead changes the subject to close out sales at the mall or the price of gas at the pump.

Today, we settle into our booth at Yorkie's for our weekly lunch date and wait for the server. Kate tightens the band on her ponytail and says for the hundredth time this month, "I really should get my hair cut." Shoulder-length and naturally blonde, her hair is flecked with white and thinning a bit on top. Once, when we were in our mid-thirties, she allowed me to wind her stringy hair in brush rollers and apply makeup to her pale face. When she looked in the mirror at her defined brows, glossy lips, and curled locks, she barked like a dog. "I look like a cocker spaniel!" So much for makeovers.

Now, almost thirty-five years later, her face remains bare of makeup, her hair still straight and anchored at the nape. We're as opposite as vinegar and syrup, me with aqua eye shadow and amber blush, thick hair dyed brown and bobbed. She wears a man's T-shirt and pull-on jeans; I choose to show off my new V-neck top and low-slung crop pants. A great grandmother, Kate has been married for fifty years. I'm divorced, childless.

We order cheeseburgers, fries, and milkshakes that we devour in fifteen minutes. "Smoking keeps you skinny," she mumbles around her last fry. "You lost more weight lately?"

"Don't think so," I say, hoping she won't preach. She's never smoked and a sign on her front door bans the habit in her house. At one-hundred-twenty-five, I'm four pounds less than last week. Of course she would notice, damn it.

She points to the sheet of paper I've pulled from my purse. "What's that?"

"I've written my obituary," I venture. "People are doing that now, you know—to get it right."

"What's to get right? Your date of birth, death, survivors, that's it."

"I want mine to read like a requiem."

"You mean like a hymn?" she asks, then pops vitamin pills and slurps the last of her shake.

"Not really," I say, leaning in. "Just read the obit and play my favorite music in the background. Dance, even." I laugh and her eyes brim with tears. "Cut it out, Kate."

She awakens each morning, she's told me, with her hands balled into fists, jaw clenched, afraid of the end of the world, weekly bills on a fixed income, one grandson's penchant for pulling out hair by the fistfuls, a ten-year-old with a bald spot up front. What would she do if I told her I had colon cancer, spread to the lymph nodes, all over? So far, only my oncologist and favorite bartender at the Oasis know. I hand her the obituary, which she reads.

Bobbie Loren Kamens loved her sister Kate and brother-in-law Robert Neely, their kids and grandkids, her lilies and limericks, Saturday evening mass before barhopping, perfect Manhattans and bingeing on burgers, her ex's and friends, didn't do doctors, treadmills, or teas but loved meditation, Oprah and opera, Friday night movies and Flannery O'Connor, blues and Beethoven, former students and colleagues at Central State College, the ones with gonads, they know who they are, and most of all sunsets, fireflies at dusk flickering over the cornfields, sleeping till noon.

Kate glances up, her eyes narrowed and lower lip trembling. "You loved *all three* ex's?"

"Sure. Ex-husbands are like old girdles, worn out but still comfortable when you're in a pinch. While we're at it," I add, "here are my funeral instructions."

"Enough already of the dying crap." She tugs at her ponytail and glances up at the clock, dabbing her eyes with the table napkin.

I press ahead, knowing she's anxious to check on her husband mowing the back acres of their home in the country. I hand her a pen and flip the obituary over. "Jot this down. After the funeral mass, hold

'Manhattans Imperfect started as a poem of funeral instructions. But then I became curious about the speaker in the poem and her sassy uptown attitude. Who is she? I wondered. Why is she concerned about her funeral at this time? I tell my students that for the reader to care about their characters, they must care first, and fervently.'

~ Barbara Zimmermann

a memorial. Invite my last ex, my favorite, and lie to his lover and tell her I liked her." Kate stares down at the pen. I jab her elbow and she starts scribbling. "Dig for the bong that I stashed in the shoebox marked 'favorite pumps.' The weed's in the coffee can, top shelf of the pantry. Mourners can toke on the terrace at Meeks Mortuary, no one will notice."

My sister starts crying. Finally between sobs, she stammers, "That's awful."

She said the same when I ran away from home at sixteen, each time I married, divorced. Ditto for the two abortions, cigarettes overflowing in ashtrays, empty bottles of Jim Beam and vermouth pitched in the trash. "But it's what I want." I pick up the tab and make my way to the register, leaving Kate to count out quarters for the tip. A few moments later, we head for my car parked at the curb, my sister's eyes swollen and red. At least she's no longer bawling.

After dropping her off, I'll stop at the liquor store, buy a bottle of Beam, bitters not needed, white and red vermouth. No matter how hard I try, though, no two Manhattans ever turn out the same, or perfect. Sort of like sisters, I guess.

I lean forward to kiss her cheek and, instead, we bump foreheads, hard. She laughs. In my mind, for a moment she's eighteen, eager to marry, and I'm two years younger, angry I'll be left on my own with our mother guzzling scotch till she's stupid and a stepfather with wet kisses and groping hands.

"Oh, Kate." I hug her to me. The tip of her ponytail tickles my nose. "It's not your fault," I say for the first time and mean it.

New Millennium Writings

Is pleased to present the New Millennium

Fiction Awards

Winning entries appear on pages 27-67 (see Contents pages)

Summer 2007

Stephen Irwin, Samford, Queensland, Austrailia, *Tail the Barney*

Winter 2007-08

Asha Vose, Knoxville, TN, *Vietnam Visits Uncle Bill*
Jacob Appel, New York, NY, *The Appraisal*

HONORABLE MENTIONS

Summer 2007	*Winter 2007-08*
Jeffrey Gibbs, Somerville, MA	Laurie Alberts, Westminster, VT
Jacob Appel, New York, NY	David Anderson, Wellington, NV
Dianne Bechtel, Rio Rancho, NM	Becky Eagleton, Tulsa, OK
Teresa Bourgoise, Los Angeles, CA	Michele Feeney, Phoenix, AZ
Gayla Chaney, Temple, TX	J. Allen Fitz-Gerald, Jay, NY
Thomas DeTitta, Americus, GA	Kristi Gedeon, Fredericksburg, TX
JoeAnn Hart, Gloucester, MA	Gertrude Simone Goodrich, Newton, NJ
Blaney Hines, Asheville, NC	Maryanne Kahn, Canberra, Australia
Sandra Jensen, Bonn, GER	Barbara Knott, Lawrenceville, GA
Meredith Levine, Easton, MA	Dahlma Llanos-Figueroa, Bronx, NY
Joshua Marcus, San Francisco, CA	John Lewter, New York, NY
J. Davis Martin, San Francisco, CA	Mary Beth Matteo, Lancaster, PA
Don Mitchell, Colden, NY	M.E. Parker, McKinney, TX
Robert Pesa, Norton, MA	Gleah Powers, Santa Monica, CA
Eric Sasson, Brooklyn, NY	Jennifer Sears, Brooklyn, NY
Patricia Stiles, Venice, CA	James Sievert, Aesch, Switzerland
Raymond Trainor, Sun Lakes, AZ	Clarence Smith, Nashville, TN
Connie Weber Bothell, WA	Lisa Sprague, Leroy, NY
Marguerite White, Northampton, MA	Lynne Stoecklein, Parker, CO
Liza Wieland, Arapahoe, NC	Lydia Williams, Duluth, GA

For guidelines to our next contest, see page 9

Stephen Irwin
Tail the Barney

I 'm not partial to travel. I'm a home body. But when Florey told me the bloke had died, I did the ring around. We three decided, out of neighbourliness and out of friendship for a chap less fortunate than us, that we'd duck out and fetch Florey's blessed thing back. But if truth be told, we didn't do it for Florey. We did it for peace and quiet.

Florey was quite the whinger.* But he was our whinger, our neighbour. That's why we nipped out that night: to flog back Florey's trinket from the dead man.

I suppose it was my dart. But let me tell you about Florey and you'll understand why Reed, the girl and I went a-thieving.

Florey moved into our block some thirty-odd years ago. It was a council relocation; he had no one to look after him. At first I was pleased to have someone new to yarn with. Florey had been around the ridges, and I don't mind a listen. But cripes, talk! This and that; war and women; won so much, lost so much. I guess we got used to it, we neighbours. Fat Reed on my left. The young girl Lisa over the road (she's new). Dimity next door: my age. We got used to Florey's deepest scratch, the one about the chap who stole his thing. His brooch, his good luck charm, the loss of which sent his whole life down the box. Yes, we'd say, that's terrible; what a scoundrel, we'd say; let it go, we'd say. Dimity suggested telling Florey to plug it, but Dimity was more of a home body than me and she was always maggoty about something. And another chap you would have a go at, but Florey had been in the war and he'd lost his legs in the flood, so I

whinger: crybaby; given to excessive complaints and whining.

27

guess we just took pity. But what would we do for a bit of shush! Well, I guess this is about just what we'd do. What we *did* do. What a night.

*

I'd had the daughter and her kids around that day. Little bastards. A chap reaches an age and I think that permits some frankness. I love my daughter, but her children are diseased little monkeys. Running around, throwing rocks, jumping the fence into Dimity's place and throwing more rocks (thank Christ Dimity's a deep sleeper or there'd have been hell to pay). They'd been swimming at Southbank, she said. Lauren talked and talked, lovely girl, but emotional. But you only get one family, so I listened politely, nodding in the right spots, tuning out of the babble and enjoying the view across the river. Finally Lauren took off taking her Godless little marmosets with her, but then Reed's family came to visit him and I had to hear all their nonsense. Why can't people speak softly anymore? You'd think with mobile telephones and all this guff people would have evolved out of yelling, but no. Anyway, come evening all I wanted was an early kip.* That's when Florey started up.

The chap who stole his brooch had died. I don't know how Florey knew this, but he come across so certain that I didn't doubt him. He'd died just this night, said Florey. He still had the brooch, said Florey. My brooch, said Florey. My good luck brooch. And the thief's family would get it now, and there was no hope then—no hope at all!—of getting it back. Woe was Florey. I patted Florey on his bony shoulders and *there-there'd* him and sent him home with the firm intention of doing nothing.

It was a beautiful night, and I would have been content to have sat out smelling the cinnamon of jacaranda bark and the tang of camphor laurel and watching flying foxes sweep like flakes of ash across the sky and watching the slow stars climb before retiring... but an idea caught me. I couldn't rest. I couldn't sleep. It niggled. It itched so I felt like ants were crawling inside me. I had a plan. I went next door to see Reed.

"Reed!" I called.

He rubbed his eyes (him tired, too, from *his* family's yammerings) and listened to my plan to go and fetch Florey's tail-the-barney brooch from the dead man. Reed hummed and nodded and rubbed his feet. "I'm not too svelte," suggested Reed, blushing. He was very

kip: nap or bedtime.

'Writing's easy. Good writing's hard. And it feels a long, long road between those poles, especially when, most of the time, you don't really know how close to which one you are. Yet, it's simple to recognise others' True North: good writing elicits powerful emotions through the seemingly effortless witchery of combining even the most commonplace words. So, on my long walk, I'm trying to convey more by saying less, to speak more clearly by listening more closely, and to write better by reading with a care that reflects the love with which stories were written. I'll let you know if it works!'

~ **Stephen Irwin**

worried about his weight. "And you're, well, you're not so young…"

"Fine," I said. "We'll get Lisa."

"Lesia," corrected Reed.

"Fine," I repeated, and we went across to get Lisa.

Lisa was maybe thirty and had moved in a few years ago. I may be old, and I may not quite have the air to fill the balloon, but I am not blind, and the thought of watching Lisa wriggling through a window was the better part of my plan, and I congratulated myself on it.

"It'll shut Florey up?" asked Lisa. Smiles never landed on Lisa's face.

I said I thought it would.

"Let's do it, then," she said. "I'll just do my face."

"No time!" I cried. "The dead bloke's family are probably there already, pawing through his things! Let's go!"

None of us thought to invite Dimity. Dimity would talk us out of it. And this was far too nice a night to be talked out of anything. So Reed, Lisa/Lesia and I went out to steal some peace.

*

In the early spring, the city's air is at once loose and tight, cool and warm, clear and full. In the pocket of the hill climbing Annerley Road one can feel toasty and pleasantly assaulted by fragrance of potato vine, cut grass and distant tweak of diesel. Crest the hill and glimpse the sparkling night time spires of the city, and suddenly you feel cold air rattling your bones, and the wind stealing all scent away to the wide, dark river, to be wicked jealously away.

And that was as far as we three got—the top of Annerley Road, looking one way North to the city and one way South to the river and all of us feeling the chill wind tugging like children—when we realised we didn't know where we were going.

We three sat in the park there to discuss notes on Florey, his bibelot, and the tormentor who stole it. Reed, puffing heavily, said he'd heard the chap who stole it lived in Taringa. I (not puffing at all) recalled hearing the dastard's name was Richard someone-or-other, and Florey was upset because the tail-the-barney was lucky.

"What do you remember, Lisa?" I asked.

"Lesia," she snarled, looking around nervously and already wanting to go home.

I said we couldn't go home. Or, we could, but we'd be condemned to years of whining and we should see this through.

She nodded nervously, hoping no one would see her with her face not made up, and explained that Florey told *her* the treasure was a pendant made in the *taille d'èpargne** style, and was given to him by a grateful gypsy when he had entered Bergen Belsen with the British at the end of the war.

That rang a bell with Reed and me.

"And also," she snipped, "the scoundrel's surname was Richard. His first name was something dull and boring."

"Bill!" cried Reed, remembering, and I grew offended because my name is Bill.

Still, we had something to start with: William Richards, Taringa, thief of a gypsy's magical tail-the-barney pendant.

Taringa, as the crow flew (and as flying foxes now did, black leather brackets arcing silently west, winking out the cool stars as they passed) was not far. But for old bones like mine, it was a fair trot. "Let's catch a cab!" I suggested, and tottered out of the deep shadows

taille d'èpargne: technique describes a process of subtle cutting or carving with the surface left mainly intact.

of the pergola toward the whirring headlights and flitting shadows of Annerley road. "Who's got some Oscar?"

Reed and Lisa looked at me blankly.

"Oscar Asche?" I asked.

Still the round, empty stares.

"Cash!" I shouted.

"Oh," they said, looking sideways at each other. *We're a bit younger than you, Bill.* It transpired that Reed didn't bring any cash—he thought we were out for a stroll which was a good idea because he was feeling heavy and unsightly. Lisa didn't have any because she didn't even have time to do her lips fergodsake let alone hunt around for her purse. And I am old, and old people in Dutton Park don't carry money—everyone knew that.

"Looks like we walk," I said.

Reed looked at his fat feet. Lisa looked up at the fingernail moon.

"What?" I asked.

Reed mumbled something about Saturday night and young ladies on their way to night clubs laughing at him, and Lisa/Lesia sneered something else about anyone going anywhere pointing at her and thinking she looked like a trollop.

I sat beside them. "You," I said to Reed, putting one arm around him, "worry too much. You've been fat. I remember when you first arrived, you looked big. But I think you've got so used to thinking you're fat, you don't realize how sporty you look. And you," I said, wanting to put my arm around Lisa but instead just patting her thin knee once. "This is a beautiful night, and it is only more beautiful with you in it, not at home sulking."

My inspiring talk did nothing whatsoever, and they both suggested they might go home.

"Well, you're not!" I snapped. "Let's walk!"

"Which way?" groaned Lisa.

"There's a new bridge across to the University," suggested fatso.

"No way, I don't do bridges," venomed Lisa.

"Well it's that bridge, or it's the Gray Street Bridge, or that other new bridge, or it's a ferry where you can have half the population laughing at you, you fat-thin miseries."

So we started back the way we came, behind the thin black shadows, behind streetlights and the thick black shadows under a clear night sky toward the new bridge.

*

Years pass fast. You think you know a place, you think you know what kind of people live here, and what kind are drawn there, but if you stay still too long, the truth washes past like a tide, carrying new things past your tired eyes. When you break free of your reef and drift with the current, you see that nothing has stayed still except you—everything is different. Hills have been subtly reshaped. Roads widened. Trees cut down or planted. People cut down or planted or transplanted. Only the stars are fixed, and they are cold and far, far away. But some things, mercifully, change slowly. Once upon a time, one wouldn't go about on foot around Dutton Park at night for fear of violent drunks. I discovered one *still* should not go about on foot around Dutton Park at night for fear of violent drunks.

"Yo yo yo!" said the young man who looked, in silhouette at least, like a penguin—all baggy britches, billed cap and swaggling arms. "Wassup wasdown wattavwehe-ya?"

I turned to Lisa and Reed, hoping for a translation. They each shrugged and took a subtle step behind me. We had been walking downhill through the park, talking about favourite foods (mine: shepherd's pie; Lisa/Lesia's: caffeine tablets; Reed's: anything starting with a letter of the alphabet) and didn't see the huddle of penguins on its park bench ice floe until we heard the voice. Then, the vapour wash of hot malcontent ran over us. The emperor strutted a bit closer. Only a circle of streetlight separated him from me.

"What did you say?" I asked.

"You a bit croaky old man," said the emperor, pronouncing the last word *main*. "You need a drink."

"Tell him to drink this!" shouted one of the shadow penguins, and I heard a fly unzip and laughter. I glanced back at Reed and Lisa. They were magically ten feet back already. I scowled.

"I don't like your attitude, boy," I said. They laughed louder. I heard metal. Once, years ago, I'd been pretty fearless. As a tar boy I'd fought one of Brophy's boys* in Charleville, and lost with great dignity. Then I grew older and scared. Why not tonight? I couldn't explain it. It was too nice a night to be scared. And I knew I would be all right. I had something to do: I had Florey's treasure to rescue, and nothing was going to stop me. All five penguins detached themselves from their nest and waddled up behind their leader.

"Righto," I said. "Rafferty rules with louts." I shaped up and stepped into the light. A siren sounded somewhere, growing louder. The boys all looked at me from under their shadow bills. Their faces were all white as sand, their eyes dark as soil. The siren grew louder. They ran.

Pleased, I looked back to Reed and Lisa. They were amazed. "Still cut quite the figure," I said, throwing a punch at the air and wincing at the grinding joints. Reed cocked his head and looked at me, then looked at his own arms. Lisa looked at me and almost—not a word of a lie—almost smiled, I swear. The bridge was ahead, arcing batwings with steel veins soaring across the river into the night.

*

We were midway across the bridge when Lisa collapsed into a tight, shrieking ball. I tried to move her, but her arms and legs spat out like snakes, one hard knuckled thing striking me in the shin. I swore aloud (which I *never* do) and limped back along the bridge, leaving Reed to the hissing viper's nest. I was cranky. At this rate we'd never get to Bill Richard's house—certainly not before his peregrine-eyed beneficiaries began their greedy sucking of things.

"What's the matter with her?" I asked Reed.

"She says she... what did you say?" He listened to her sizzle a moment. "She says she jumped off a bridge and that's why she hates them."

I rolled my eyes, put my hands on the cold rails, and looked out across the river.

It was a beaut. In my time I'd see the Yarra, the Torrens, the Margaret, the Gordon and the Mary. This wasn't a pretty blue brook, or a wild rapid antelope. This was wide and stately and slow to anger. She glimmered in the moonlight, a grand diva hiding her bulk behind shimmering silver and twinkling ice blue. Her mangrove flanks smelled like tears. I could just make out the cemetery, and the new galvanized steel rails of the roadside that separated the graveyard's ivory tombstone teeth from the black, plunging banks. There. That must have been where Florey lost his legs. Where he lost his trinket, and his luck.

As the river mumbled quietly below me, I let my mind drift back

---

*__Brophy's boys__: Fred Brophy's Boxing Troupe toured Australia staging bouts in search of new boxing talent from among the locals.

with it. Ten, twenty, thirty years. Back to 'seventy four. And the floods. I remember the council men, wandering about, digging new holes while the rain thundered down. Laughing and occasionally vomiting, stomachs disgorging as their trucks disgorged. The river had swollen with the rain, rain, rain, and she'd grown very fat and hungry. She'd broken the banks in some spots, eaten the banks in others, one of them here at the cemetery. She'd risen up to the level of the tombstones and started chewing into the cemetery soil. You've seen film of icebergs shedding their sides and crashing into the sea? This was like that, only brown not blue. Slabs of soil, undermined by the racing brown-gray water, suddenly fell away into the current, exposing new, raw banks. From these began to poke caskets. The fierce rain would trouble the rotting flanks of coffins until they fell away, exposing the rotten linen and gray bones of corpses. Some caskets fell whole into the torrent and bobbed away, to be found days later caught by mangrove fingers or bouncing expectantly against flooded doorways in Eagle Street. But most simply filled with water and snatched shriveled cadavers into hurried and unwelcome baptisms. The council were alerted to this problem. It wasn't a health problem; not compared to the bloated cows and bloated dogs among the flotsam. But it was a problem of perception. Bony hands and spidery legs and surprised skulls peeking out from the riverbank was unattractive to nose and eye. They got in teams to exhume swiftly, and relocate the bodies before the river could. They were only half in time for Kenneth Dougal Florey. His coffin happened to be aligned in such a way that his feet hung out over the new drop created by the voracious waters. He lay there, pants ripped away, embarrassed as hell, half hoping to be saved and half hoping to be spared the shame by being pulled into the current. As was Florey's lot in life, he got half what he wanted. His white phalanges, then metatarsals, then talus bones, then left fibula and right tibia then both femurs were sucked away before the two council workers got to him. It was William Richard who knelt on the bank, reached down, and yanked what was left of Florey up and out of his second, fetid womb. "He pongs!" shouted Richard, tossing the half-skeleton to his co-worker Dennis Chee, who giggled and caught Florey in an army surplus body bag. Florey was, naturally, doubly embarrassed by his aroma.

"Wait a second," shouted Richard over the rain, and Chee stopped zipping. Richard sloshed over and reached down.

"No no no!" Florey told me he shouted, but the rain was too loud. Richard plucked the necklace and the beautifully wrought pendant from Florey's neck, snapping the silver chain.

"You a dobber,* Chee?"

Chee said Florey shook his head. "No, Mr Richard."

Richard winked, and—for Florey—everything went black.

Others in their stygian cocoons in the back of the lorry told the fluttering and incensed Florey that the bloke's first name was Bill— that's what the chink called him when he wasn't in strife, said one— then a furious argument over racial invectives drowned Florey's pleading for help to regain his *taille d'èpargne* pendant. The next day, Florey was moved into the row opposite mine, high on the hill. He'd been an insufferable whinger ever since….

"Here, Bill!" Reed's voice pulled me back into the cold night. He'd somehow gotten Lisa/Lesia to her white feet, and had one arm thrown around her thin shoulders.

A silly wave of envy wriggled through me.

"Here!"

I hurried over, my own feet tack-tacking on the hard bridge surface.

Lisa was shaking, sounding like a dozen frozen, chattering jaws. Reed and I exchanged a nod, and I put my arm around her too, my bones creaking as we took her weight.

"It's all right, Lesia," I said. "We'll have you off here in a jiff."

"Story Bridge," she whispered. "Story Bridge. Story Bridge…"

I remembered, now, what Dimity had told me when Lesia had first moved in. She'd jumped from the Story Bridge, but the tide had been out and she'd landed head first in salty mud. She'd suffocated to death. It was rude, but one day he'd glanced at her stone:

> ***Beautiful daughter***
> ***Loving sister***
> ***Taken too soon***

"Here we go," I said, and we were over. But I kept a hold of her long after we were back on land, until she stopped shaking.

*

*****dobber**: One who dobs, that is, informs against or implicates others to authority.

We walked through the university grounds, three unlikely hay-stacks of white shuffling between pools of light, footsteps echoing like dice rolls off the hard stone walls. I stared up at the buildings, feeling the wind tickle inside me. Till now, I thought I'd seen a bit and done a bit. But all these big square buildings, filled with books and those computers and God-knows-what else, made me feel like I hadn't done a tap. I felt small.

"We need a phone book," said Reed.

"Oh! I should call my sister!" suggested Lisa.

Reed explained we had no money, and Lisa nodded glumly.

We tick-ticked through the sandstone canyons. We only saw one lad, one hand on one hip, gently swaying while he relieved himself against something that was either a rubbish bin or a sculpture.

"Fella!" I called. "We need a telephone directory."

He turned, saw us, grinned and held his head, and went back to contemplating his stream. "Fuck me," he giggled.

We found a bank of glass booths near shuttered doors. The directory was chained to it, a ragged and beaten dog of a thing, and looked up *Richards, W.* There was only one in Taringa, in Pike Avenue. We'd get directions as we got closer. We kept walking, and I was pleased to be out of that dismal mausoleum place.

*

We passed houses glowing prettily and warm as Tilley lamps. The Methodist church was dark. The Catholic church was lit, and singing came from within. I slowed. Human voices carried on the soft breeze, rising like fresh tide and falling like clean rain. How long had it been since I heard music? How long since I heard voices in joy, voices other than Dimity's or Florey's or Reed's, or my daughter's dripping weariness or my grandchildren's bored snatchings? How long since I'd heard voices talking without bitterness or confusion, with hope and brightness?

"Bill?" said Reed, tapping his wrist. I nodded and we pressed on. The she-oaks in the school yard whispered as we passed.

"Look!" said Lisa, delighted.

On the bitumen parade ground, two dogs chased each other, tumbling. The smaller one grabbed one of the bigger one's ribs and ran off with it. The bigger one scooted after, bones and nails clicking. Lisa laughed and jumped the fence to chase the dogs, throwing the errant rib. Reed and I leaned on the fence, watching her.

"Makes you wonder, doesn't it," said Reed.

"About what?"

Reed's dark sockets were thoughtful. "What happens to us. After we die."

I watched him. "This comes next," I said.

He looked at me. "Oh. Yes," he nodded. "Forgot."

I called to Lisa: "Come on, sunshine."

She was grinning, breathing hard. Her smile was as lovely as I'd imagined it would be, and that made me a bit glum. "Come on."

*

The smells! One becomes so used to the back palate of fresh cut grass, the front palate of fresh flowers, the mid-palate of distant salt or distant exhaust fumes. One forgets the smells of life. We passed houses, and we three sniffed, grinning at each other:

"Wood smoke," said Reed.

"Mosquito coils," said Lisa/Lesia.

"Rissoles!" I moaned, licking airy lip. Oh, rissoles and fresh beans and butter! And here: steak and chips! (Porterhouse, specified Reed, and Lisa and I believed him). Lamb and Brussels sprouts. Coffee. Muscat.

We floated on aromas, nudging each other. Reed shook his head. I saw him run white fingers down a belly he remembered, growing sad.

"Don't worry," I said. "This is window shopping. It's free!"

He nodded gloomily, and I looked at Lisa. She shook her head. I changed the subject.

"So, why do you think Florey misses this bauble so much?"

We compared notes, each digging into our lightly whistling heads for memories of mostly-ignored, one-way conversations with Florey. The pendant was beautiful, rose gold with black enamel tracery. When he and the other Brits had stumbled stiff-legged through the gates of Bergen Belsen, some of the walking skeletons had stared, some simply died with the shock of the horror ending, some had wrapped leather and bone arms around the soldiers. One had simply walked up to Florey and pressed the curio into his hand. Florey hadn't known if the naked thing was a man or a woman

"Once, once!" the creature had said, and winked, its smile revealing two teeth. "Romani. Yes? Good, good." And held up one twig finger—once! This we agreed.

The second thing we agreed was recalling that Florey had wondered how long the thing had been in the gypsy's arse.

The third was that, when he'd been demobilised, he went to a jewelers in Suffolk and talked a deal on a gold chain.

That day—that very day he put it on!—had been the luckiest day of his life. In one day he, first, met the most beautiful woman he'd ever seen (who, ahem, became his wife); second, was feeling so lively at meeting Imogene that he put one pound neat on a horse named—can you believe it?—Lucky Day, on the nose, at fifty-to-one and it *won!* And third, he took that money, wandered into a card game in The Old Bell and got a straight and won the keys to a very posh Ford Anglia de Luxe and a handful of petrol coupons! Happiest day, happiest day…

"And then what happened?" asked Lisa/Lesia.

We didn't know. He ended up here. He ended up broke. He died alone, buried by the Serviceman's League.

"Here," said Reed, pointing.

An old man was walking up the footpath toward us. Reed elbowed me. Lisa elbowed me. I stepped forward. "Good evening," I said.

The man stopped and looked up. "Evening." He smiled. "Lovely night," he said. He wore a cloth cap and carried a white cane.

I agreed it was, and asked him if he knew where Pike Avenue might be?

Down the way I was heading, left at the corner, one right one left and there we were. Then he straightened.

"You've not come for me, then?"

I heard the tremor in his voice. "What makes you say that?" I asked.

"You three click when you walk, and your voice sounds like wind blowing through old bottles on a forgotten beach. But aside from that, you seem very pleasant."

I told him we were not coming for him, but thanks for the directions. He waved his cane with a cheerio, and kept walking.

*

This was Brisbane as I remembered it. Weatherboard houses with flaking flanks or proud gloss beige and white, hunched on spindle legs with batten skirts and dark tin bonnets, kind-eyed windows winking at a mild night where high-hissing gums and spider-fingered jacarandas scratched at the southern cross, polishing her bright. A wide fig spread her skirts over the whole road, knitting the breeze with her dark leaves. The houses were tucked behind hedges of roses, hedges of geraniums, low wire fences, low white timber fences. We started looking for the house the phone directory told us held the remains of William Richard. We didn't have to look hard.

The house was gray and in darkness. The yard was overgrown, wind-dried grass a foot high crunched like steel wool underfoot. The ancient paint on cottage's fibro shanks flaked like eczema, and the down-pipe was rusted through, hanging like a rotten tooth from the diseased gum of the equally rusted gutter. The place stank of bad luck.

"Well, we beat the family," said Reed.

"Or they beat us," suggested Lisa.

"Here," I said, and pointed to the overgrown path that bled toward the lattice veranda doors. The grass was unbent. We were first.

"Nice work, Sherlock," said Lisa, and winked emptily at me.

I smiled and pressed the doorbell. No sound came from inside… but we all felt the loose air of regret shift around us. I didn't like this too much.

"We could tell Florey it was gone," suggested Reed. His voice shook. Lisa nodded and skipped back toward the street, decided already.

"No," I said. "We ought to try." Bones do not have good grip. The green brass doorknob slipped under my fingers. "Bung idea, this," I said. "Round the back."

Stepping high through grass dry as ash, we crept along the narrow yard under the yawning shadow of the unhappy house. At the back, a low set of sagging stairs rose to a bent landing and a tattered screen door.

Lisa/Lesia nodded at me. *You go first.*

One, two, three steps, and I was rapping softly on the aluminium frame dusted white with age. "Richard?" I whispered. "Bill?"

Lesia and Reed stared back at me, white skulls tiny moons on shrugging shoulder bones.

"Fine." I pulled the door open and crept inside.

Some homes are graves of the living. They are dust and sorrow. Lost time hangs like a caul, strung by cobwebs. Skittering things hide under dishes unwashed (who will see them?), clothes unfolded (who will mind?), floors unswept 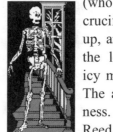 (who will visit?). A calendar from 1989 was crucified by one rusty nail to the hallway wall. I crept up, and four clacking feet followed mine. Ahead was the lounge room, a tiny box, a lifeless place split by icy moonlight slivered by dust-caked Venetian blinds. The air smelled of stolen tobacco, mice, and loneli- ness.

"There," whispered Reed. Curled like an unanswered question mark on the floorboards was a man evaporated.

"Bill?" I asked.

He blinked, staring with white, already sinking eyes. "Yes?"

"Bill Richard?" asked Reed.

"Jesus, Reed, seriously," snapped Lesia.

But the dead man answered anyway, "Yes. I can't move."

"That's 'coz you're dead," said Lesia.

Bill strained and turned his head a notch, and saw us. A whiff of rot, of surrendered lungs, a sigh of surprise. "Oh."

We told him who we were, how we knew Florey, and how we'd come to fetch Florey's tail-the-barney pendant. As we did, Richard's dead hand crept like a crab up from the floor, across the broken reef of his chest, to his throat, where it curled around something there on a chain. There it nested, guarding.

"It's my good luck charm."

"It's not yours."

"It's mine!"

"You stole it."

"No!"

"Give it over!"

"Never!"

We all pried at Richard's closed crab hand.

We all four saw the yellow headlights flash across the front door glass; we all four heard the car door outside slam. A moment later, the front gate creaked. A moment after that, knocking at the front door. Through the dirty rippled glass, the silhouette of the visitor. Reed, Lesia and I were perched above Richard, exchanging looks.

"Ssh!"

"SSSH!"

"*You* be quiet!"

"Quiet!"

We listened. We waited. The visitor knocked again.

"Dad?" she said.

I looked down at Richard. "Oh," he whispered. "Oh, no."

At the front door, keys jangled.

"Hide!"

With an ivory clatter, we scurried. Lesia ducked behind the dusty genoa lounge. Reed cried "I'm too fat! I'm too fat!" and ran down the hall to the toilet. I stood quietly, and crept back, back, back into the dark corner of the room. The front door groaned open, and the woman slipped inside.

"Dad?" She clicked the light switch, on-off, on-off. "Dad..." she whispered, disappointed, unsurprised. She stepped deeper into the musty, hollow coffin room. And saw the curled rag figure on the dusty floor. Her breath sucked in sharply, and her steps were fast. She knelt over the body, hands fluttering like birds... then perching still. "Oh, Dad..."

She was maybe thirty, maybe a bit more. She wore a skirt and jacket and shoes slender like calligraphy on her feet. Her hair had been worried by the wind. Her face was in shadow. She sighed, and it sounded like relief. "Hello," she said, quietly.

No, no! I thought.

She touched his covetous clam hand and uncurled it easily. Again, her breath sucked in, and—had I lungs—mine would have, too. For even from across the room I could see the tail-the-barney, and it was beautiful. It was gold, dark gold with a hint of sunset and warm as fire. Its surface stretched with sensuous curls of black enamel, fine as hair mussed in love, but in the shapes of delicate vines that wrapped around a cunning gate that would, if gently pushed, open to a summer garden so breathtakingly lovely one would never, ever leave.

"Daaad...," she whispered, and reached for the clasp.

Then I saw it. She'd put it on. Next day would be a wonder—a day of love and luck and laughter. But the day after would be duller, and poorer. The next, anxious and desperate. The next, worried and angry and clutching. The next, the next, the next... until she was curled in rags, empty as a kettle and alone as a dry well in a desert.

"You can't have it," I said, and stepped from the shadows.

She looked up at me. Her eyes widened. Then they rolled back in her head and she fell to the floorboards with a bang and puff of cinnamon dust.

"Nice one, Bill!" said Lesia, rising from behind the couch. "Kill her?"

"What was that bang?" shouted Reed, scuttling up the hall.

I hurried to the girl. I touched her wrist. I touched her white, soft throat. Reed and Lesia hovered above me. I felt... and found the lovely thudding beneath her skin. "She's all right."

"Well, get it, then!"

Her hand was tight around the pendant, just as zealous as her father's.

"She won't let it go!" said Richard.

"Shut up, you!" I hissed. "She's your daughter? Want her to end up like this? You ungrateful man, neglectful, ungrateful..." I stopped a moment, and thought of my beautiful Lauren and her dirty marmosets. "This is not yours," I whispered.

Then, the girl's eyes fluttered open, and found a focus. I am guessing what she saw was a bit much: three creamy skulls staring down at her, sockets wide and dark and full of wonder. Because her eyes rolled back again, and she hit the floor with a second solid thud.

"Nice catch, Bill," said Lesia. But the woman had released her grip. I snatched up the pendant.

"We'll see you, William Richard," I said.

"You're thieves," he hissed.

I shepherded Reed and Lesia toward the front door. "Wait," I said. "Reed, here."

"What?"

I took him by the arm, and led him into Richard's bedroom.

Against the wall was a duchess, its walnut veneer lifting like tiny tectonic plates, its mirror back smeared with dark melanomas. "Here," I said, and led Reed to it. "Look." I positioned him before the glass, and made him see himself.

For a moment, he was still as a crane, staring. Then, one hand lifted to a double chin that was gone, then slid to a belly that had vanished, then idled to buttocks that had sublimed into history. "I'm not fat," he whispered.

"I know," I said, and Lesia and I smiled.

"It killed me. Heart attack."

I shrugged, "Well, you had to die sometime."

Lesia and I watched the smile dawn on Thin Reed's wide, white face.

"Come on, mate." I tugged his arm, and we flew before the girl could wake again.

*

We rattled down the streets of Taringa, clicked up the footpaths of St Lucia, covered Lesia's eyes with careful fingers and crossed the bridge, and slipped like white wind through the trees to the cemetery.

"Florey?" we cried. "Florey!"

Florey mumbled awake. "What? What?"

"Close your eyes and open your hand," said Lesia.

He scowled and didn't, so she punched him and stalked home. I watched her go.

"Night, Lisa."

"Lesia," she snapped, but when she turned back she was smiling, so that was good.

"Well?" demanded Florey.

"Reed?" I asked, and Reed put the pendant into Florey's hand.

"Oh!" cried Florey. "Oh! OH!!" He clasped his hand tight, he opened it wide, he held the pendant high, he hugged it close. "Isn't it beautiful! Oh, it's beautiful! Did I tell you how I found it? It was 1945, and I was with the Eleventh—"

"Tomorrow, Florey," I said.

"Yes, yes, tomorrow," he fluted, spinning in the moonlight.

I stepped away and looked at Reed.

He smiled at me. "Thank you, Bill," he said.

"Maybe next week? Another trot?" I suggested.

He nodded. "I'll tell Lesia."

"Good night, Reed." "Good night, Bill."

Dimity was waiting. "Well, husband?" she demanded.

"Well indeed," I replied, and kissed her and we held hands and watched the stars do their slow wheel, and sank into the cool earth to sleep.

Asha Vose
Vietnam Visits Uncle Bill

U ncle Bill never tells the truth exactly, but he does *tell a story. The story pushes out of his tin-roofed, almost-house. It opens the broken screen door that bangs like a shotgun twice every time you close it, no matter how carefully you do it, even if your fingers are softer than moth's wings.*

Inside his house in Nowhere, Mississippi we are sitting around an oak table, eating instant mashed potatoes and pork chops because Uncle Bill, an old-school bachelor, can't freeze an ice cube. We are heavy from Grandma Norma's funeral. As a little girl, I used to dig with her in the garden, and the smell of the fresh earth was like an embrace. Now the bottoms of our Sunday black pants and skirts are stained mud red. We are relieved to hear a story that doesn't start, "Norma was a good woman." We carry the funeral in our pockets.

Uncle Bill leans over the table. His shadow stretches over the wood as he says, "In Saigon the lights bleed arterial indigos and varicose violets over the streets, and in the open market the stench of rotting fish pulses the sky first baby pink, then cement, and finally thrombosis blue. You cover your nose and mouth with your shirt-sleeve, but nothing can protect you from that stench. It's a smell as though every dead thing on earth sat up and said, *Ahh*." Over the dingy school-globe in my mind the story settles in Saigon, Vietnam. I picture thin letters over a pink, cardboard world. This is a side of my uncle I don't know well.

Uncle Bill rests a moment and lights a cigarette. Years of hand-rolled tobacco have left him with a voice like smoky gravel. As a gentleman, he knows when to pause in his story, and how to let the

An earlier version of Vietnam Visits Uncle Bill appeared in Harpur Palate.

 *'Writing short stories is about complex emotions and questions. It's a process of crystalizing What If into a narrative, or illuminating truth from a ghost's point of view. When you are writing you get to fall in and out of love with your characters, give them their own shoe size, or expand the universe for them. I can't imagine anything better.'*

~ **Asha Vose**

smoke drift over him lazily and hang above his head. He clenches the cigarette tightly between his index and middle fingers. He turns the cherry toward himself and glances at the glowing ember eye.

"It's not like you see in the pictures," he says. "Don't believe those pixilated smiles. The women don't always wear straw hats and not everyone grows rice.

"At night we went out to let off steam. I had a knot in my stomach then, watching the night-women sell their precious dark, and wondering which girl might be the last I ever touched. We were out there all alone. We had that in common. We were the lost children of a shadow city." Uncle Bill leans back in his chair and looks out the window at the murky sky. "I am not afraid of the shadow city," he whispers.

As the words leave his lips and pass through the smoke they blacken and twist into the long curving outline of her. First the indentation of her waist is a column of smoke at the back of his head, her proud ribcage giving way to immature breasts and thin arms. The curling dark outlines of her widow's feet appear after her torso.

Hollow-eyed and long-fingered she steps from the smoke. Her long, night-colored hair spills over his shoulders. She leans in until they are cheek to cheek. She places a single translucent finger over his lips and whispers to me... *My story.*

Mylai the beauty, I know this is her story. I don't know her real name, but Mylai is the name of a place her heart once lived. I am afraid of looking at her too intently. I fear her massacre eye. I fear her mother's kiss. I fear the tall embrace of her.

Uncle Bill trembles slightly as her finger caresses his lips. He can't feel her fingers, but he knows something is wrong. She has come from the other side of the war, a lost piece of his memory, and he refuses to see or hear her. He takes a long drag and pulls himself up straight in his seat.

"I was eighteen. After six weeks of basic training they sent me. The morning I flew in, the sky was the color of scrambled eggs. I'll never forget it. They made me a gunner for a Medevac. They wanted me to shoot the people that shot people who were wounded. Everything in the jungle seemed like a bad dream. The life expectancy of my job, Huey Medevac gunner, was two weeks," he says.

Mylai says, *My brother Lua was seventeen. He was tall for his age and clumsy. He could fish better than all the other boys, but they still teased him. They always teased him because of his teeth. They used to call him River Rat.*

"I had an M16. It jammed constantly. When I picked it up, I thought the last thing I'd hear in my life would be click. Click," says Uncle Bill. Mylai's smile turns down at the corners as she rests her head on his shoulder.

Then Viet Cong took him. There were no more fish. I went down to the river in the morning with my little wooden hooks and sat on the bank. In the slippery light every boy had a split-toothed smile, and every silver line led back to my brother.

"I didn't see him until the Medevac had been shot down. Six of the guys weren't moving. Stone dead. The pilot was out with a head wound. He was heavy on my shoulders as I was stumbling into the green, and I heard shots like hot thunder all around. I could feel the pilot's blood glue each hair to the back of my neck, tight to the skin. Up in a tree, I saw the sniper, a blink of black in the leaves."

There is something the sniper doesn't know about Uncle Bill. Actually, there are several things: He doesn't know the taste of the crunchy pecan ice cream Bill will eat, or the satisfaction Bill will feel lying in bed in the hot afternoon as the breeze twitches the sheets. He will never feel the fur of the soft, soft dog Bill will keep tucked in his coat pocket in forty years. But the most important thing he doesn't know about Bill is that boys from Nowhere, Mississippi, shoot like the devil.

"I pulled the pilot behind a rock and propped up my M-16. The whip-crack sounds echoed in the jungle for a long time. I had never killed a man before—sure foxes, squirrels, deer, but never a person. I carry that sound with me like a weight on my index finger," says Uncle Bill. "I didn't see his face. They sent me a letter. I was supposed to get a bronze star. I don't even know his name."

Mylai digs her nails into his cheeks and pulls her head off his shoulder. She releases his face, crossing her arms as she turns her back to him. For a moment, she looks as though she will just walk off. Her hair twitches angrily, as she turns and walks around to face him. She kneels in front of his chair and puts her hand on his.

His name is Lua, my little river rat, she hisses, *and he has our father's eyes.* Mylai's eyes are solid black as she turns. *They never gave you your star. They don't even pay you enough for coffee, old man! The bills fall like bombs on your table. No more Agent Orange and no more money for orange juice,* she sneers.

"We woke up one morning on the wrong side of a war," Uncle Bill says, as if he's heard her. His story has etched the lines in his skin a little deeper and bleached the white in his hair whiter. It has deepened his gravelly voice to a croak and given his eyes a milky sheen. If it keeps up this way he will be blind before he finishes telling it.

They crawled into my home on their elbows and bellies, stabbing the yellow dirt then smoothing it back again. Her eyes are normal as she stands and walks behind his chair. She has released Uncle Bill's face, but the half-moon bruises where her nails were remain on his cheek. She brushes dirt off his shoulder, almost lovingly.

They took everything.

He begins to say, "They said when we came home..." but she looks at him brightly, dementedly, now all smiles as she cuts him off.

What if I could give back what they took away?

"... We'd be heroes," he finishes.

Mylai the Beauty closes her eyes, places the very tips of her long fingers on his forehead, and breathes out a long exhalation of smoke over Bill.

Uncle Bill's wrinkles peel off in curls and glowing peach-soft skin grows in, his ears move up and shrink back. Wispy hairs thicken and grow black over his head, jaws move up and cheekbones re-emerge, but his smiling white-blue eyes are the same. He is twenty again. My uncle is handsome. I have seen the pictures, and I believe the smiles.

Mylai opens her eyes. She is translucent now, and when she turns I see the glimmer of moving smoke in her fingers held over his hand. She moves her lips next to his ear. Even though he can't hear her, she whispers softly, fervently to him as though every word were an incantation.

You met me on the bank of the river. You saw something flash in the water, and you followed the silver line to me. You gave me something dark. It melted in my mouth and tasted like love. The sky was the color of scrambled eggs. I'll never forget.

You took me to the States to get married in your family chapel in Hattiesburg. I wore your sister's wedding dress pinned close to my waist and arms. We moved to Tupelo, Phoenix, and Charlotte. I was pregnant before the spring and our children bloomed as fast as rain: first Anne Marie and Camille, then Edward our little king. The little ones painted pictures with their fingertips. On Fridays you took out the trash, and on Mondays I brought in the milk. She smiles as she cries, a dreamy smile that doesn't quite reach her eyes. Her lips brush his ear as she whispers.

You never lived alone in this almost-house. You didn't marry Sandy the gold-digger that took your barbershop. You never watch children on the swings a little longer than other men. You didn't skid your car into a telephone pole that night, bursting it open in a ball of flames and glass.

She points down at his ankle. *Your bone wasn't charred black past mid-marrow, and the patchwork veins never healed over like blue cracks in your whitewash-tinted skin.* She slumps in front of him on the floor, overcome by the years of what might have been.

"Heroes," Uncle Bill mutters still thinking of the war. "I don't even think they know what heroes are." He stretches his legs as older men sometimes do, as though they might meet resistance. He stubs out his cigarette. There is only the faintest limp in his right leg as he stands and moves to the window. The clouds have cleared and the sun shines faintly on his shoulders.

We are stuffed as the ducks Uncle Bill keeps on his mantle. My Mother has served the black coffee that keeps us awake, but our eyes are closing. We are pointedly ignoring the dishes. Some of us are thinking of Grandma Norma's bathtub merlot and the twinkle-splash it made against the white tub wall as she stirred it. Some of us are regretfully remembering Uncle Bill's mattresses as too soft or quite hard. We are not fussing over Uncle Bill, telling him he should sit down or save his strength. We are tired of massacre eyes and cardboard worlds. We are ready for bed.

It seems as though his story is floating along in mid-air, drifting like a cloud. It wants to dip and dive or soar up into the sky, instead condemned, it hangs. We wait in the silence, each of us listening to the sound of our own heartbeats. Uncle Bill, silhouetted against the streaming light of the sun, dust motes gleaming around his shoulders, the echo of blood sloshing during ventricular contraction, rapidly turning red-blue. Mylai spread like a fan on the dirty floor, shoulders heaving, the flow as the valve opens and blood rushes into the oxygen, turning bright red. It seems in this sunlight as though nothing will happen, as though nothing has ever happened. We can hear our blood turning blue.

Uncle Bill's story, the pulse-less thing, refuses to die. It sits around the room looking back and forth. It thinks, "What was that noise? What's happening over there? Is Uncle Bill OK? What's going on?" The heat has made it jumpy.

I am not sure how I know we are waiting for an ambush, but I can feel the tingle of adrenaline like needles in my fingertips. I want to yell, "Stop it! I can't go back to Vietnam. I'm half-asleep!"

But Uncle Bill has no choice. Vietnam, home of the bomb-children, isn't a place he goes. It is a place that creeps in on him, as he gets older, casually taking a few minutes in the supermarket when a display falls over with a crash.

Outside the window, a twig snaps. The water in our glasses trembles as though the house were shaking. A porcelain mug slips from the shelf and shatters into a dozen sharp fragments, then bamboo stalks explode through the floor, ten feet tall, full-grown and yellow-skinned. Their leaves unfurl and twist over Uncle Bill's shoulders. He stands immobile as vines scramble along the floor, scale his legs, and cinch in his waist. Uncle Bill turns a blind eye to the bamboo, ignores his vine-belt, and gazes out the window as he lights a new cigarette.

A bamboo pole smashes into my elbow and shoots past my head at an angle. The bamboo is growing, denser and thicker, until the crimson light of Uncle Bill's cigarette is the only part of his outline I can see. I hold my throbbing arm to my side. The roof blows off of the house as though it were made of cloth, wrinkling as it flies away. The sun shines blinding white. Uncle Bill is speaking again. I try to hold onto his voice but he's muffled by bamboo. Tripwire crisscrosses the room like a spider web. Each of the walls, one after the other, falls flat with a boom. Mylai is moving through the bamboo like a shadow. I strain to hear the soft growl of Uncle Bill's voice in the jungle. I want to get up and search for him, but I'm afraid of tripwire.

"There never was a shadow city," he says. From his voice I know he has found something he lost, and lost something he never knew he had. My eyes search for him in the bamboo so uniform it makes me dizzy, yellow and black and green and yellow and black. The sun, the insufferable sun, has mutated into an interrogator determined to illuminate every crevice. I catch myself before I wipe the sweat from my forehead. The silver tripwire above my forearm winks up at me.

"I called it 'the shadow city' because I couldn't call it what it was. The other men called the Vietcong Charlie for C, but I did it to have one name for the men, women, and children. I didn't want to see their faces. There were many of us soldiers, but one Charlie," he says. "I pushed away all memory of that place and her."

Mylai steps from the bamboo to stand between Uncle Bill and me. He is finally ready to see her. He turns his head and looks at her for the second time in forty years. "On the last day I saw you, you were running on the mainland away from the village and your hair flew behind you like a flag."

The first time I saw you, I wanted to kill you, and take from you what your people had taken from me. But you had the rifle.

"I could see you weren't afraid of me, but you didn't stop. You put your fingers together like a pistol and laughed a high laugh. 'Bang! Bang! Joe!' you said, as you ran into the bush. I knew we had taken something from you by the sound of your laugh that hung like a familiar weight on my index finger." His hand doesn't shake as he holds it out to Mylai. In an instant he is an old man again, but his white-blue eyes are the same.

"I could have believed your smile. I would have grown rice," he says.

You couldn't marry me now if you wanted to. You would be trying to love all Vietnam in one skinny girl. She turns and walks through the bamboo, fading with each step until she is another shadow.

Mylai's words echo in the room, as Vietnam leaves as quickly as it came. The bamboo falls through the floor and the floorboards fill themselves in. The walls right and join with the roof as it straightens. The dying light outlines Uncle Bill and his cigarette. We are back in his house, heavy in our seats watching him look out the window as his story plummets to the ground shrieking. In its death throes it unravels long brightly colored ribbons: fuchsia, canary yellow, forest green, periwinkle. I catch a scarlet one as it spins out of control. As it slides between my fingers, I have a vision of where the story ends. It ends in Norma's house with Bill's father, Grandpa Vinson, a few months after their son returns from Vietnam.

Grandpa, his leathery hide silver in the moonlight, pulls his body out of bed at two in the morning. He grasps his shotgun with hands that do not tremble, not even during WWII when he slept in a ten-foot deep grave. His knobby knees protrude from large white shorts. He looks at his son waiting for him, silhouetted in the doorway. Bill is also knobby-kneed and in his shorts, but sweaty, unable to sleep. Grandpa knows there is nothing living in the darkness outside. He looks at his son. He cannot tell where the shadow ends and his son begins.

"I'm ready for Charlie now. You just show me where you heard them," he says in a soft voice. They walk out the front door and into the flowerbed circling the house, searching for something they will not find in Grandmother's irises.

Jacob Appel
The Appraisal

"Sixty-three," said Abbie. "It feels like only half a
life." She stood at the open window and gazed
through the bars. Outside, the city pulsed in its usual
frenzy.

A street merchant had spread his wares on the sidewalk in front of
the school—books, records, baseball memorabilia. Across Riverside
Drive, a dark-skinned nanny wheeled two light-skinned babies in a
perambulator. Farther down the block, an elderly Chinese couple was
shaking the branches of the ginko trees. They did this every June,
collecting bucketfuls of the soft, stinking fruit. Abbie wondered what
they did with the fruit, but she'd never gotten around to asking.

"They're making progress every day," said Bert. "All sorts of
advances."

Abbie turned to face him. "It's funny. I can remember when
anything past sixty seemed absolutely ancient." She surveyed the bare
classroom. In one corner stood the boxes of picture books and art
supplies that belonged to St. Mary's. Two smaller cartons, marked
PERSONAL, would go home with her. "Did you know that when my
grandmother turned eighty, she received a framed certificate from
President Truman?"

"You can fight this," said Bert. "Don't croak on one doctor's
opinion."

"To what end? To die like Leonard?" asked Abbie. "I won't go
through that."

She'd married Leonard shortly after Bert divorced her.
(Sometimes she quipped she'd lost one husband to another man, the

An earlier version of The Appraisal first appeared in New York Stories.

'I feel no shame in admitting that I often draw inspiration from the writings of others, particularly writers of my own generation whom I greatly admire. I vividly recall reading Emily Rapp's brilliant and breathtaking essay, Surviving the Body, and feeling called upon to explore the question of how one can draw political or social meaning from physical limitations. Here, in The Appraisal, my hope was that Abigail's spiritual world would grow as her body diminished... and then the geniuses in Washington supplied an endless war as a convenient backdrop for her spiritual growth.'

~ **Jacob Appel**

other to another world.) Leonard's final months in the chronic care facility—she called it the *gulag*—had been wretched. He'd suffered a series of small strokes. Each carried off a piece of him—as water smoothes sand.

"Is there anything I can say?" asked Bert. He was sitting on her desk, his short legs dangling over the side. Much of his hair was long gone. The orange tufts at the corners of his scalp resembled giant earmuffs. "What haven't I thought of?"

"I asked *you* that, once," answered Abbie. "Remember?" That had been the morning he'd revealed his relationship with Wesley, an episode now almost inaccessibly remote. She crossed the room and settled beside him on the desktop. For the first time in thirty years, she took his hand in hers. "It's too late to say anything," she said. "I know what death's about. And I'm not afraid of it, not terribly. But to end up alone in a sterile white room with a handful of meager possessions—*that* scares the living shit out of me."

Bert nodded, polishing his forehead with his fingers.

"I've thought everything through," continued Abbie. "Having a tumor in your lung makes your mind work overtime." She liked to imagine the growth as solid but delicate, like the heart of a songbird. That, of course, had been months ago—before the diagnosis, before the cancer slithered into her bones. "I haven't led the life I wanted," Abbie said.

"You've taught all these children."

"But I didn't change them. Not the way some teachers do." For years she'd labored at it, but teaching wasn't her gift. Her wit confused the children. Eventually, she'd given up trying. "It was a waste. I want my death to have meaning," she said. "Like the heroes I teach the children about. Like Joan of Arc and Anne Hutchinson and Nathan Hale declaring, 'I regret that I have but one life to give for me country.'"

"To raise awareness," agreed Bert.

Abbie squeezed his hand. "In a way. Please don't think I'm crazy, Bert, but I'm going to set myself on fire."

Bert said nothing, at first. Abbie stared down at her toes, then across the room at the globe and the filing cabinet. Under the American flag, the oscillating fan whirled with silent grace.

"To protest the war. Like during Vietnam," Abbie explained. "I know I've led a mediocre life. I'm not a fool. But what's that quote from Ralph Waldo Emerson? *Consistency is the hobgoblin of little minds*. Well, I'm going to do something inconsistent for a change. Something *grand*. I may have lived a mediocre life—at best—but I'm not going to die a mediocre death."

"You're serious?"

"Dead serious," she answered. "That's why I called you."

"You can't do this," said Bert.

"I can do this. I *will* do this. And I need your help."

*

The idea had come to Abbie at the beauty salon.

Usually, she had her hair done around the corner. Her stylist, Vin, was a no-nonsense gay kid from the streets of Baltimore. He worked quickly. He had steady hands you could trust not to lop your ears off. Both of his grandfathers had been barbers back in Sicily. She'd always thought his shop cozy, a blend of Old Neighborhood and Old World, but now, with the claw of death reaching for her across the horizon, it struck her as drab. *So much* of her past, her present, suddenly seemed drab—as though she'd lived, unknowingly, to the wattage of a low-energy bulb. Maybe that was why, on the morning after her diagnosis, Abbie walked past Vin's window and crossed Amsterdam Avenue to the glitzy salon that had replaced the Filipino laundromat. She'd craved change. She wanted to spend money frivolously.

All of the furniture in the new salon was black and angular. The women waiting ahead of her were half her age. Abbie sat down. She pulled *The Forsyte Saga* from her canvas bag. The book seemed excessively long. Was it worth the investment? It might be the last book she'd ever read. The girl in the next chair, a bleached blonde with an eyebrow ring, was reading *Beyond the Perfect Orgasm*. Maybe that was a better choice. Or possibly Proust. Unable to concentrate, Abbie folded shut her novel. A conversation between two of the stylists caught her attention, though several seconds elapsed as she laced together its threads.

"But would you do it?" asked the stylist nearest the window. She was a sharp-featured young woman who reminded Abbie of an angry pigeon. "I mean if there were no personal consequences. If you could walk away scot-free."

"Fuck, Summer," said her male coworker. He was tall and emaciated—what Abbie called *concentration camp chic.* His voice rolled in waves. "Where do you think up these questions?"

"They just come to me," said Summer.

Summer snipped at the bangs of an unsmiling brunette, cutting more empty space than hair. Her work struck Abbie as impersonal. Like getting trimmed by a topiary gardener.

"Think about all the suffering he's caused," Summer persisted. "You would have killed Hitler, wouldn't you?"

"Jesus Christ," said her co-worker. "I don't know."

It suddenly registered with Abbie: These kids were talking about assassinating the President. Abstractly, of course. But none-the-less a statement about the plight of the world, about the lunatics she would no longer live to see destroy it. This was the second time she'd over-heard strangers discussing the President's death. The previous week, she'd had dinner with a retired colleague. The couple at the next table, clearly on a first date, were debating the appropriate response to learning that the madman in the Oval Office had been shot. *He'd* said glee. *She'd* insisted upon relief. Halfway through the meal, they were kissing. Meanwhile, Abbie's companion lamented a world gone to hell in a hand basket. "When JFK died," he'd said, "I lost a brother." When Kennedy was shot, Abbie had been younger than the stylist.

"I'd do it," said Summer. "I really would."

Her coworker signaled for the next woman in line. "So it's settled," he said.

The brunette rose from Summer's chair. She was closer to Abbie's age than the stylist's, attractive, though the skin of her face looked too tight. "I don't think you should kill anybody," she interjected. "Ever." Her voice held a deep sadness. "If you're upset with things—and there's certainly enough to be upset about—you should put *yourself* on the line. Like Gandhi or Martin Luther King."

"I guess so," agreed Summer.

The brunette stepped around Summer. Abbie assumed her place in the chair. When the woman had paid and departed, the male stylist said: "Way to upset the customers."

"Screw you," said Summer. "I'm still right." She scooped up Abbie's hair in her bony hand. "What are we going to do today?"

"Not much," said Abbie. "I want to look like Grace Kelly."

The stylist smiled blankly. Abbie felt old and useless.

"Just a joke," she said. "Whatever you sense works best."

Already, though, she was thinking about putting herself on the line. She'd never done anything *particularly* political before, but the need had never seemed so great. Besides, it would help make up for frittering her life away. That, after all, was what she'd done. She'd never opened up that catering company, never gone back for her doctorate. Instead, she'd passed her days keeping things in their place And there'd been so many minor crises—dripping knapsacks, bruised elbows, valises left on airplanes....

And now Leonard was dead. Her parents were dead. Her son, Norman, was as good as dead—she hadn't spoken to him in a decade. (The boy hadn't even come to his father's funeral.) For years it had torn her apart, had nearly torn her marriage apart. She'd tried visiting him once, in prison, when he served time for passing bad checks. He'd have none of it. Another of her failures. Thinking about Norman made Abbie miserable, so she no longer did.

Summer massaged shampoo into her scalp. "Do you think you'd like some color? Maybe a hint of vermilion?"

"Yes," said Abbie. "Whatever."

She was recalling the first time she'd seen Leonard teach. He'd been a bioethics professor at Columbia. "Do you know what this is?" he asked, holding up a strand of rope. He paced the lecture hall, sweat beading at his temples. "Not any old string," he declaimed. "Not your run-of-the-mill, butcher's block string. No, no, Nanette! This is my *lucky* piece of string." Here Leonard had paused, leaning forward over his lectern. The veins bulged above his temples. Perspiration glistened at the end of his nose. "If you intentionally destroy my lucky piece of string," he demanded, "to how much compensation am I entitled?" And then he'd asked about human life: What was it worth? How was "Grandma"—unemployable, of limited social use—any more valuable than his lucky piece of string? Abbie's first husband, Bert, was an appraiser of artwork and collectibles. But Leonard—Leonard had been an *appraiser of lives*.

"Maybe you should kill yourself," said Abbie.

The stylist was still kneading Abbie's head. "What, honey?"

"Self-immolation. Don't kill the President. Kill yourself in protest."

As she said the words, they struck Abbie as surprisingly convincing. Later—when she shared her plans with Bert—she would realize how much easier it was to make the decision than to explain it. She'd compared it to coming up with the idea for a bedtime story. "It wasn't there. And then it was." Eventually, if you told yourself the story enough times, as she would do over the coming weeks, its every thread seemed inevitable. These reflections, of course, would come later. Sitting in the salon chair, her hair matted in lather, all Abbie knew was that she'd found an alternative to a death of quiet desperation. The previous night, she'd counted barbiturates in preparation for a private end. Now a public departure rose before her, a dramatic gesture. That was the sort of hook you could hang your life on.

Abbie drew her head up. Soapy water trickled down her back.

"What the hell?" exclaimed Summer.

Abbie rummaged in her purse. She closed the girl's hand around three crisp twenty dollar bills.

"Fuck, honey," shouted Summer. "What's wrong?"

"I'm dying," Abbie answered, smiling.

She brushed past the stylist and hurried outside. It was a bright afternoon. The sidewalks were crowded. Some pedestrians glanced uncomfortably at Abbie, but most ignored her. She didn't care. She walked home briskly, trailing water and suds up Ninety-First Street.

*

Bert's encounter with his ex-wife left him jittery. When he'd driven down to meet Abigail at St. Mary's, forty miles south of Chatham Valley, he'd hoped to knock off other errands. A college friend had recently acquired an étagère at a rummage sale. The man thought it might be valuable and had asked Bert to take a look. Also, Bert wanted to buy fresh oysters for Wes. And then there was the forgery case in which he was to be an expert witness, one of the perks of semi-retirement. For weeks, the lawyers had been on his back about dropping off the affidavits. Before visiting Abigail, Bert had planned to wipe clean his to-be-done list. Afterwards, of course, he'd been useless.

He found Wes out in the yard, digging a trench around his vegetable garden. This was the latest salvo in his war against woodchucks.

"You're home early," said Wes.

Bert dabbed his brow with his handkerchief. "What's that old Chinese curse? May you live in interesting times."

"That bad, eh?"

"Worse."

Bert recounted the morning's trauma. Wes continued to dig. He'd slung his t-shirt over a wooden fencepost, baring the lean muscle of his chest. At seventy, Wesley Rockford was still "the straightest gay man in the lower forty-eight." Sport fisherman. Hockey fan. One-time petrochemical engineer. (He claimed that in his native Alaska, some gay men were even straighter.) Wes had lost three fingers in a childhood hunting accident, leaving a right hand like a vintage baseball mitt. When he shoveled, he used only his left arm.

"It wasn't just the cancer," said Bert. "Or the suicide plan. It was all of it together. You had to see her there in that empty classroom—Those stacks of tiny chairs—Good God! She looked so...."

"Diminished?"

"Yeah," said Bert. "Diminished."

He sat down on the grass, using his jacket as a pillow. That portion of the lawn had been newly mowed. Later, Wes would rake up the clumps of fresh chaff.

"Abigail's mother was also a smoker," added Bert—to no particular purpose. "She also quit too late."

Wes kicked a clod of dirt off his shovel. He picked up a stone and lobbed it into the hedge. "Are you asking for advice?"

Bert shrugged. "Who knows? It hasn't sunk in yet."

"I imagine it hasn't. Are you sure she was serious?" Wes kneaded his lower lip between his fingers, a sure sign that he was concerned. "I never thought of your ex as so political. People have a way of talking when they're under stress—and they really don't mean anything by it."

"She was serious. As hard as that is to believe. Jesus Christ! This is something Buddhist monks do, not New York City school teachers." Bert wiped a tear from his eye. "Her sense of humor hasn't changed though—for better or for worse. She said that even a chef as bad as I am can rustle up Abigail Richmond flambé."

"I'm surprised she asked *you*. Doesn't she have anybody else?"

"Apparently not. Or maybe I wasn't her first choice," said Bert, although privately he was sure that he was the first person, the *only* person, that Abbie had asked for help, and this touched him deeply. "I guess she's at the end of her rope. Desperate times call for desperate measures—and all that."

Wes tossed his shovel into a mound of red earth. He settled onto the grass, resting the back of his neck against Bert's abdomen. They lay in silence. Wes's head rose and fell with Bert's breath. Bert knew they were sharing the same thought: How grateful they were that they were together—*that Bert had left Abigail.* Cleaning the attic the previous spring, Bert had discovered the letters he'd written to Wes in Alaska. Their urgency stunned him. Certainly, he'd never loved Abigail so intensely.

He ran a hand through Wes's thick gray hair. "I suppose I owe it to her," he said.

"You don't *owe* her anything," answered Wes. "But you should stop her."

"I don't know. It's not that simple."

"You're not actually thinking of helping her, are you?" Wes sat up, his shoulders and neck rigid. "Are you out of your mind?"

Bert looked away. A bank of clouds rolled across the sky. Others hunkered at the horizon. Darker clouds, the color of steel wool. As a child, he'd had a knack for finding secrets in clouds—rabbits, dragons. In Pelican Bay, Florida. A long time ago.

"Don't think crazy," said Wes. "You can't go around setting people on fire. You could go to jail, Bert. You could ruin our lives."

Wes was right, Bert realized. Wes was nearly always right. It could ruin their lives. But hadn't he once done far worse to Abbie? "Let's go inside," he said. "Before it rains."

*

This was the first year of Bert's semi-retirement. Their friends had warned him against this arrangement. When you're ready, they said, go whole hog. Half-retired was like partially pregnant. Often, it meant premature idleness. Time would weigh heavily upon him. The reality—in his case—had been decidedly the opposite. He'd had too many offers, not enough hours in the day. He still undertook special projects for his former employer, the city's leading auction house. Insurance companies offered him lucrative consulting fees. A niche publisher wanted him to lend his expertise to a line of coffee table books. Bert didn't delude himself. He wasn't a household name. But by hook and by crook, he'd risen to the top of his field. Not shabby for the self-taught son of a pawnbroker.

"Maybe I feel guilty," he told Wes. "My life worked out. Hers didn't."

They were walking up Broadway toward Abigail's building. They were late. Parking had taken forever.

"Count no man happy until he dies," quoted Wes.

"Meaning?"

"It's Oedipus. Greek for 'Don't jinx us.'"

Bert grinned. He pressed Abigail's buzzer. Her building didn't have an elevator, so they walked up the six narrow flights of stairs. "Thank you for doing this," he said as they reached the topmost landing. He squeezed Wes's hand. "Thank you for *understanding*."

"Nobody said anything about *understanding*, Bertram, but I do love you—so if you're going to insist upon making a mess of things, I'm going to try my best to minimize the damage."

This was good enough, thought Bert. That first evening, Wes had argued and cajoled and pleaded. *What did Bert know about self-immolation? Wasn't he afraid of the consequences?* But Bert's partner was a practical man. When it became clear that Bert was seriously considering a part in this folly, Wes determined to keep him from getting caught. He'd insisted upon coming along to see Abigail—as much to keep an eye on Bert as to vet his ex-wife's plan.

Abigail greeted them at the door. She kissed Bert's cheek, shook Wes's hand. "Catch your breath," she said.

"I forgot how steep those stairs are," said Bert, coughing.

She laughed. "The cost of high ceilings."

The flat was just as Bert remembered. Tasteful, a tad stuffy. Walls and walls of Leonard's books. Several of the volumes were quite valuable. First editions of Freud, of Benjamin Rush, of Lister's essay on inflammation. A glass and mahogany bureau housed the sterling silver tea service that had once been Leonard's mother's. There was also a good share of kitsch: commemorative porcelain, bead bouquets, watercolor seascapes. The apartment's most interesting fixture—although of minimal commercial value—was a life-size plastic skeleton. It hung opposite the Laz-E-Boy recliner, where one expected to find a television set.

Abigail steered them into the dining room. She followed moments later with a tea pitcher and a plate of scones. "How long has it been, Wesley?" she asked. "You look spectacular."

"You do, too."

She poured tea. "For a woman on the verge of death?"

Bert and Wes exchanged looks. Abigail had always been a pale-skinned, curveless woman—but in a comely, country-lass sort of way. Now she looked sallow and stiff like a tarnished candlestick.

"Take anything you want, by the way," she said. "I know there are some books that interested you, Bert. Help yourself."

"You know I can't do that," said Bert.

"Why not?" snapped Abigail.

Bert spooned sugar into his tea.

"I can't take them with me," Abigail persisted. "This isn't Ancient Egypt."

"You'll outlive us all yet," said Bert.

Abigail held her teacup only inches from her lips. "*No*," she said. "*I won't.*"

Bert added another spoonful of sugar to his tea. He took a small sip. It was too sweet. This visit no longer seemed a good idea. He'd hoped having Wes along would calm his nerves, but he wasn't as comfortable with helping Abigail as he'd claimed. He'd taken her to the high school prom, after all. And deep down, although he was grateful to Wes for tolerating this insanity, he realized that he was now mistreating Wes as he'd once mistreated Abigail. It was *their* life he might ruin. Not just his own. At the same time, a part of him sympathized with his ex-wife's plan. He *did* understand. Unlike Abigail, he had been political. He and Wes had rallied against the epidemic in the eighties. They'd marched for Matthew Sheppard. They'd done their part. And over the past month, he'd also become obsessed with the war news. He watched non-stop, religiously, hoping the conflict might end. If there were no war, there would be nothing to protest—no reason for Abigail to kill herself.

Other men might have searched for guidance in religion, or psychiatry, or the classics. These had never been part of Bert's life. Instead, he'd tracked down Abbie's son in Utah. First, Norman had hung up on him. When he phoned again, the son called him a shit-packing faggot. Bert saw no reason to mention this encounter to his ex-wife.

"Wes and I are thinking of traveling," said Bert.

Wes threw Bert a puzzled look. Abbie smiled. "That's terrific," she said. "You've certainly earned it."

"Does that mean...?"

She shook her head. "I can work around your schedule."

Bert reached his hand into his trouser pocket and fumbled with his keys. His strong suit was property, not people. As hard as he tried, he had a difficult time drawing a connection between Abigail and the bloodshed overseas. *Everybody* he knew opposed the war. It was something you opposed in the abstract—like inequality or injustice. But that didn't mean you had to sacrifice yourself. Abbie didn't even own a television. He doubted she could name both of their United States senators. Now that he was actually in her apartment, discussing her suicide as casually as a birthday party or retirement dinner, he wanted to shake her. To tell her that she was the second most important person in his world. To say how empty his life would be without her jibes, her quotations from Emerson and Whitman, her ravenous laugh.

Instead, he asked: "When?"

"Not just yet," said Abigail. "What is it they say after casting-calls? Don't call us, we'll call you."

*

Abbie saw no need for immediate action. Occasionally, reading the names of fallen American servicemen in the morning newspaper, or contemplating the larger number of unreported foreign casualties, she was seized by a twinge of regret. Might she have saved these people? Had she cost some poor mother her son? But Abbie wasn't fool enough to believe that even her public burning could single-handedly alter national policy—that anything she'd have done would have mattered. Her goals were more modest, long-term. Also, she wasn't ready to die.

The first weeks of July, Abbie devoted to practical matters. She broke down her apartment as she'd done her classroom. Drawer by drawer, shelf by shelf. It amazed her how much junk she and Leonard had acquired over the years. A pair of pack rats. Now she gave it all away. The silver tea service and the medical books would go to Bert; she'd arranged it with the lawyer. Anything else of value—and who knew what had value these day!—was to be sold, the proceeds going to St. Mary's.

Abbie double-checked the perpetual upkeep on her parents' graves, gave the Dominican superintendent his Christmas tip on Bastille Day, bid silent farewell to her friends. Her death would be messy, explosive. She hoped to leave her affairs tied-up and tidy.

If anything scared her, it was the pain. At the age of eleven, she'd stuck a paperclip into an electric outlet. She still had a scar on her index finger. This, she feared, would be far worse. But as she learned more about Thich Quang Duc and his Vietnamese monks, about Jan Palach in Wenceslas Square, she discovered that self-immolation—like most specialized skills—had its own artistry. You couldn't grit your teeth and bear it, as you might an injection. The trick, it appeared, was to lose yourself in a fugue state. One authority compared it to long-distance running. Through much of August, Abbie explored the subject. She sat in the small island of lindens and plane trees, at the juncture of Broadway and West End Avenue, reading about Afghan brides and Tibetan monks and the Ananda Murga cult. If she'd had time—if life had taken another course—she might have pursued these studies academically. She could already envision the shape of her dissertation: chapters on Indian sati rituals and Turkish Kurds. But Abbie sensed she was growing weaker. She had trouble maintaining her balance, forming fists. Some days she didn't make it to the park or even out of her dressing gown. According to her oncologist, the cancer had spread to her brain.

Several times, Bert phoned. Dear Bert. "Just to check in." He wanted to discuss the war, but truthfully, the details of the fighting didn't interest her. She knew it was wrong. Deep down. *That* was what mattered. Why should she care for particular battles, the names of interchangeable generals? In college, she'd been rebuked for hazy thinking. Her history professor regarded her as pleasantly vapid. (Many years later, she'd run into the same professor at Tanglewood. *A third-grade teacher*, he'd said. *Important work.* She'd wanted to claw his eyes out.) If it were possible to miss anything once you were dead, she would miss Bert. His decency, his lavender handkerchiefs that looked like dinner napkins. And she'd miss children. Their tiny fingers, their solidarity. Being a second-rate classroom teacher, it was Abbie's curse to love young children so terribly.

The morning after Labor Day, Abbie rose early. She'd stayed up late the night before, enjoying the final pages of *The Forsyte Saga.* (She'd read somewhere that John Hinckley and Mark Chapman had carried *The Catcher in the Rye* with them. Maybe, she'd told Bert, she could inspire a new trend.) Outside, the air was damp. A nip of autumn already hung in the breeze. When Abbie arrived at St. Mary's, the children were already getting off the buses. One after another. In little yellow raincoats, carrying brown bag lunches. The light was on in Abbie's classroom. Through the bars, she could see the walls layered with construction paper. Orange. Green. Red. She walked to the payphone on the corner and called Bert.

It was time.

*

Bert picked Abigail up at the curbside. She wore tan slacks, a beige blouse, a matching kerchief. Her trademark canvas bag hung over one shoulder. She couldn't have weighed more than ninety pounds. On the phone, Abigail had warned him to expect the worst— but nothing could have braced him for the fragile steps, the bony cheeks, the sharp sinews exposed in her neck. Overnight, his ex-wife had suddenly become an old woman. A woman *beyond* a certain age. When she reached the car, he'd had to go around to help her close the door.

"Did you have any trouble?" she asked.

"Smooth sailing," he said. "So far."

He glanced in the rear-view mirror at the stack of press releases. These were to be distributed afterwards. The most critical resource, three canisters of gasoline, he'd concealed under a blanket in the trunk. Wes had provided him detailed instructions about covering his tracks—on the importance of handling the gas canisters with gloves and of shielding his license plates with burlap. Wes had purchased the envelopes for the press releases at a stationery shop in the next county, afraid the FBI might trace the paper stock. He'd warned Wes to deposit them in multiple mailboxes. He loved Wes for taking on this deranged mission as his own. Yet even as they'd kissed on the doorstep that morning, Bert sensed that Wes was hoping he might reconsider. He nearly did.

"I'm glad it's September," said Abigail. "I've always looked forward to September."

Bert started the ignition, but drove slowly. "We could stop for some coffee," he said, as casually as possible. "Wait for the weather to clear."

"Wait until I lose my resolve. Is that it?" Abigail rolled down her window and surveyed the rain with her palm. "Barely anything. Just a drizzle."

They eased their way down Broadway. Block by block, light by light. Both of them aware that Bert had chosen the slowest route. On the drive from Chatham Valley, he'd had so much to tell Abigail. About him. About her. About them. Now his mind had gone blank. "Wes said to send his love," he said.

"Please thank him for me. I always liked Wesley."

Traffic slowed around Columbus Circle. Jaywalkers darted through the intersection. Cabs honked. Abigail had selected the front steps of Federal Hall for her departure. Across from the Stock Exchange. The site of Washington's Farewell Address. She'd considered City Hall Park, Ground Zero. (It was like choosing a venue for a wedding, only cheaper.) Ultimately, she'd sought a place without children. A vacationing family, she'd feared, might break her nerve.

"Maybe we should have had kids," said Bert.

Abigail smiled. Her eyes glowed. "Maybe."

Bert considered reaching for her hand, but didn't.

After that, they rode in silence. Bert watched Abigail while they drove. She gazed out the window, her hands folded in her lap. When they reached the Financial District, she said, "In *War and Peace*, Pierre almost assassinates Napoleon. But, in the end, he doesn't have it in him."

They were stopped at a traffic light. Bert turned to face her. He expected to see tears in her eyes, but they were dry. "If I don't have it in me...." She looked at him helplessly. Her hands were shaking. "Hush," he said. "It will go fine."

*

The night before, Wes had painted the gasoline canisters black. From a distance, they looked like stereo speakers or lighting equipment.

They parked several blocks away—as far as Abigail could walk—and Bert carried the fuel along Wall Street. They advanced slowly, at Abigail's limited pace. The rain had tapered off, leaving a residue of soggy wrappers on the steps of Federal Hall. In one corner, a woman Abigail's age fed pigeons. A band of twenty "permanent" anti-war protestors stood entrenched behind a nearby police cordon. Several wore tie-dyed t-shirts, shaggy beards. Others were better dressed, including one elderly man with a bowtie. They occasionally waved their political placards. Across the street, behind an identical cordon, an even smaller pro-war faction marched solemnly in a narrow circle. There was a young man in a naval dress uniform and a handful of homely, overweight girls draped in American flags. Bert genuinely felt badly for them—as he once had when he'd heard eighty year-old Barry Goldwater interviewed on public radio. Yet at least they believed in *something*, he thought, however misguided. Across the street, at the Stock Exchange, the lunchtime crowd was starting to file onto the streets.

"I'm not good at farewells," said Bert.

"Who is?" asked Abigail.

She handed him her canvas bag. How decisive it felt to take it from her. Soon enough he'd be meeting Wes at their bridge club, the alibi they'd chosen, and already the claiming of the body, and the funeral, and the plans for a spring unveiling—all carefully mapped out by Wes—now seemed inevitable. Nearly *fait accompli*.

Bert struggled to find the right words for the moment, but some moments were beyond mere words. Abigail nodded in the direction of the anti-war protestors. "The competition," she said.

"For you," answered Bert. "Absolutely no match."

Abigail smiled. She retrieved a tiny self-striker from a small rectangular box.

"The *perfect* match," she said, holding it up. "Now step back."

Abigail eased herself down to the steps and poured the gasoline over her head. First by tilting the canisters, then lifting them as they yielded weight. She might have been a small child enjoying a public bath. Bert couldn't bear to watch. He felt nauseous. He jostled his way along Wall Street toward Broadway.

Behind him, he heard shouting. He caught a glimpse of the flames reflected in the plate glass of a bakery window. It was done.

Now he was to dispatch the press releases and then meet Wes at the bridge club in Chatham Valley. Instead, he continued walking, running. He'd lost track of where he was heading or why.

He found himself crossing through Battery Park, approaching the water, the canyons of Lower Manhattan receding behind him. Songbirds flitted in the trees. Wes would have known their names. Across the harbor rose Ellis Island, The Statue of Liberty, New Jersey. Several small children were playing in the wet grass, illuminated by a thin white beam of sun. Bert stopped to watch them. It was a perfectly tranquil moment, the sort Abigail had treasured. This was why she'd sacrificed herself so willingly—not for an abstract peace, but for a moment just like this one, a moment of genuine grace for Bert and for humanity. You could close your eyes, and listen to the children's laughter, and imagine that nobody, anywhere, had ever died.

Don Mitchell
Slip Pivot

"*G*o *ahead and ask the question," Toni's son Alec said. "I guess. Well. How long?" Elliot said into the phone, stomach lurching at the words he had thought but never spoken.*

How long. All summer and fall he'd been talking to Toni on the phone two or three times a week, sending her things he'd written, saying he'd come to Geneva to get her and bring her to Buffalo so she could see his new house. But she'd been saying she was too weak. Maybe when she got better. During the five years he'd known her, she always had gotten better.

Nobody had answered her phone for days. Each time he'd only gotten the machine, which meant she was back in the hospital. He'd been leaving cheerful messages: "Hi, it's me. Just checking in. I'll call again." So he hadn't been surprised when the phone was finally picked up and it was Alec, the son who lived in St Louis. If Alec was in Geneva Elliot knew the answer.

"A week, ten days, maybe less."

Elliot couldn't speak for a moment. Even if it wasn't unexpected, he hadn't known how he'd respond when the time came. "Oh, man," he said, the banality of his response amplifying the pain. "Oh, shit. Sorry." He stopped, unable to think of anything to say.

"She wants you. Will you come?" Alec asked.

"I can come the day after tomorrow, OK? Then I have to be in Boston. But I can stop by on the way back, too. See her twice."

"Come both times. The boys want you too. Something about their computer."

Elliot hung up the phone and looked at his screen, letting his eyes relax their focus, which didn't matter because they were already

'I wrote Slip Pivot in 1997, soon after the death upon which it is based, but waited ten years before sending it out. Sometimes the piece is ready but the writer isn't. I began writing in college but chose an academic career instead of taking a shot at being a writer. When I started writing fiction and poetry again, three decades later, it was the woman who became Toni in this story who first published my work. She gave me my start as a writer, so it's immensely satisfying to me to have her live on as a character in my fiction.'

~ Don Mitchell

blurring. He had usually been sitting at his screen when he was on the phone with Toni, because he was usually working on something and wanted to talk about it, or had been doing email with her but wanted more immediacy. And now with her death a certainty, on a timetable, here he was looking at a screen again. It felt comforting, as though nothing had changed.

He'd been doing the same thing the first time he'd talked to her. The phone had rung and a woman's voice he didn't recognize had said, "I'm calling about the poems you submitted. I'm sorry I didn't get back to you sooner but I've been diagnosed with cancer and I've been setting up treatments and things."

"What kind?" Elliot asked without thinking.

"Ovarian. The worst." And then she'd told him she'd publish his poems if he made a few changes.

Later, he marveled at how oddly their relationship had begun. There had been no before-the-cancer that changed into something else. No period of ease that was then disrupted. He'd never known her when she hadn't been endangered. It wasn't that the danger had hovered over her, casting darkness, a pall; he didn't think either of them had felt that way. There had been a starkness, he thought, as if the danger had been strong light coming at them from a low angle, throwing everything into sharp relief, heightening contrast. Right from that first call they'd never been tentative with each other, and maybe that was context more than personality.

Elliot sat rocking in his chair, remembering how they'd finally seen each other in the flesh. It had been at a meeting where they'd both been going to read poetry to a likely indifferent and possibly hostile audience of academics.

"How will I recognize you?" he'd asked on the phone, "As for me, I'm fifty, and bald."

"So am I," she laughed.

Before he left for Geneva he made her an arrangement of the newly-tasseled variegated grasses from his yard, some red leaves and pods, and a dandelion he found still alive among the prickly pear. He chose a brightly colored Panamanian card and wrote her a note: *I love you with grasses and leaves, and with this dandelion, brave and beautiful in November.*

*

Cars were lined up in the driveway. He took the arrangement and went to the door. Three dogs greeted him, barking and scuffling, nails scraping on the hardwood floor. Only one of them knew him, the one she'd gotten as a puppy a year ago. Alec greeted him, saying, "Sorry about all the dogs. I had to bring mine, is what happened. They're doing all right together but the cat's freaking."

"How is she?" Elliot asked, as he leaned over to pat the dogs, who were milling around. Even the strange ones seemed happy to be petted.

"In and out, because of the morphine. I'll get her ready for you."

The other kids were in the kitchen, a person he didn't know was in the living room, and he could hear movement upstairs. Elliot sat with the younger boys and waited.

"We can't get this new game to run," said Anthony, the ten year old.

"What is it? What happens?"

"It's called *Blood*. Actually, we can't even get it installed."

Elliot started to make a face, then caught himself. "Blood?"

"We know. It's not exactly a Quaker game, but our father sent it and we want to play it."

"I'll help you after I see your mom."

When he walked in, her eyes were open but unfocused and she seemed unaware of him. He was startled by her appearance, not because she was so thin—he expected that—but because of her hair. All the time he'd known her she'd been bald or nearly so, but here was thick, black hair. Short, but thick. It was a sign of how long it had been since he'd seen her, how long since the last chemo, the time he'd sent her a fleece jester's hat.

"Just wait," Alec said, "when she goes away it's only for a minute or two. She'll be back. Sit and wait."

Elliot put his arrangement on the bedside table and tried to sense what might be in the room with them. He hadn't been in a room with her very many times. He had stopped by every time he'd been near Geneva, but that hadn't been often. Elliot thought of their connection as Victorian—intimates out of a Trollope novel, exchanging notes and letters, manuscripts—but of course it was all electronic. Most mornings there was something from her, usually written after midnight. Her email address. He wouldn't be typing it again. The phone number programmed into the auto-dialer. How long before he'd bring himself to delete it?

He didn't sense struggle or alarm in the room. On the phone, in email, she had always seemed battle-ready, even fierce: *The beast is out of the cave again*, one email had read, *time to take up the sword and fight.* He replied with some lines he'd picked up somewhere— Greek?—*The night is gone, the sword is drawn and the scabbard thrown away.* The next time he visited there was a naked kung fu sword on the wall. He asked her if she'd thrown away the scabbard and she answered with a simple *Yes*.

But when he was alone with her the air around them always seemed soft, even tender, and sweet. He never sensed her shielding herself from anything. Settling into her presence reminded him of deplaning into an open-air Hawaiian terminal, of lurching, stiff and tired, from the stale, metallic aircraft atmosphere into open tropical air, mantled by the fragrance of plumeria, edged with the smell of jet fuel. Instead of masking the kerosene odor, the flowers rendered it irrelevant.

He felt the same thing when he came to her. When the two of them were together, something compressed the beast and moved it aside. It never disappeared but, like the jet fuel, became irrelevant. Elliot thought she was somehow able to draw energy from him and

71

cloak herself with it so she could let down her guard. Elliot didn't believe in mystical energies but he knew what he felt and sensed, and kept his mouth shut about it.

Even a hospital could seem a hopeful place when he was there with her. After one surgery, he sat and read her a story, one about how he'd scattered his father's ashes; she'd known he was working on it and asked him to bring it. "It's beautiful," she said when he finished, "Now help me with my IV and we'll walk around the ward a little bit and then I'll try some tai chi."

But once that spring, the successful-surgery spring, the sweetness hardened and cracked, the way carelessly-heated sugar can pass unnoticed through caramel and coat the saucepan with brittle, bad-smelling black. Elliot was sure it had been his fault. Sitting at her kitchen table he'd said, "You know, I think you've beaten it, I do."

"Don't say that!" she spat at him, "Don't ever. You can't say that," heaving a great sob, a thing she had never done in his presence.

"Even if it's true, look what it's cost me," she said, slamming the palm of her hand on the table, spilling her tea, "Not my hair, hair grows back, but the rest of me. I'm hardly a woman anymore, am I? Important parts of me are gone and others don't work. Stuff I cared about, you know, is useless. I'm alive but I feel old and ugly. So if they cut all of it out of me that's fine, fine! but right now it seems worth it only when I know I'm still in the battle.

"If I think *I've beaten it* then I have to think about what I lost doing it. The cost. As long as I'm fighting I just go on but Jesus, I'm such a wreck. You never saw me when I was beautiful, I never say things like that, you're making me say it, but you never did. See me. And I was. And my hair. It was amazing. I miss my hair the most."

"Well, that's what I think, anyway," Elliot said, not wanting to back away from what he'd said, thinking if he did it would be the same as saying *OK, you are going to die then*, "And what's left of you still makes quite a woman. I'd take you any day."

She blew her nose, and tossed the tissue over her shoulder onto the floor, not even trying to hit the trash. Not even cleaning up the spilt tea. "See? The rules of engagement say you get to be messy." Then she smiled, and laughed, bringing back a kind of lightness, though the sweetness, spooked or shy, stayed out of the room. "And you know what? That woman of yours in Binghamton's going to dump you. I can tell. So maybe you'll get your chance at me, hey? Maybe what's left of me isn't so bad. Some of my parts are better than yours. *Your* hair's never going to grow back."

Elliot laughed and ran his hand over his head. He wanted to stroke her head, too.

She stood up and turned a figure across the table from him. "I'm dancing better than ever now, by the way. You should come to my class sometime and learn to waltz with me."

"I'm a lousy dancer," said Elliot, staying seated, "I don't know why. I can't seem to relax. Even as a teenager I was terrible."

And in that way *beaten it* was dropped, but Elliot picked it up again and put it on a photo. He had taken a picture of her on that visit: back-lit so you could see her stubble, she was standing in a tulip bed, holding daffodils she'd just cut, looking straight at the camera, an enigmatic expression on her face. To Elliot she seemed calm and purposeful, even secure. On the back of the framed print he taped a note: *To a strong, wise woman who'll look at this picture when she's old, and remember.*

What I see in your picture, she wrote back, *is a ravaged middle aged woman who's been granted a reprieve.*

*

She moved her head a little and smiled at him. "You've come." Her hand was resting on the covers. He took it in one of his. Her skin was smooth and full, not slack and dry, which surprised him.

He picked up the card he'd brought, and showed it to her. "Read it to me," she said, so he did, but it was hard and he had to stop twice. She didn't seem to notice.

Perhaps, he thought, perhaps his speech had fallen into the same cadence as her attention and so had been seamless to her.

"I like the dandelion," she said, "turn it towards me. People bring hothouse flowers. Wild things are better now."

She closed her eyes and went away. Elliot sat, holding her hand and looking at her. In a moment Alec came in and raised his eyebrows.

"Just a couple of minutes more," Elliot said, "please."

He kept holding her hand, watching her dream, thinking *the friend of my heart*, which is what he called her to distinguish her from the other women in his life. He couldn't just let go of her hand and leave. He wanted to kiss her, and when he rose to do it she woke.

Leaning towards her he said without thinking, "I have loved you," the tense surprising him with its acceptance, its finality.

"I know you have," she said.

She lifted a thin arm and put her hand on the back of his neck. He steadied himself with one hand on her pillow. He meant to kiss her forehead, to brush it with a kiss and leave her. But she tilted her head back and moved towards him, pressing her lips to his, her mouth open slightly. He could feel the little gusts of her breath. He put his hand on the thick black hair he had never felt, and stroked it. Her lips were full and moist. *How can this be?* he thought. When he pulled back slightly she pulled him down, kissing him strongly, even ferociously, rising a little more, kissing him hard, harder, then released him abruptly, fell back onto the pillow and closed her eyes.

There was a sudden commotion downstairs: dogs barking, storm door slamming, the high piping voices of children excited in spite of themselves. Elliot stood up, seized by the moment, wanting to stay in it. Concentrating on Toni took all his strength. If he gave in to the noise, it would collapse around him, ushering in disorder and its partner, death. If he could possess this moment she had given him, then afterwards he would always be able to distinguish it from others, superficially similar: bending over a woman lying in a bed, her night-gown falling open a bit, as Toni's had when she rose to kiss him, a breast curving beneath cotton. The times a woman had kissed him, leaving early for work, or going home.

He wanted to keep this memory from mixing with the others. Maybe if he gathered it in, inhaling the scene as if it were air; once in him he could force phase changes: gas, liquid, solid; it would harden, perhaps crystallize into something to be held and examined when he chose. He looked around the room trying to fix everything in his memory.

She opened her eyes and when she located him she said, "I was dreaming. I was dreaming about you, that you were holding the dandelion in front of you and I was looking at it, and you were walking away from me, walking backwards down a hallway or a path, then I couldn't see you anymore but I could still see the dandelion."

Elliot started to say, *Wild is what's left,* but before he could, she closed her eyes again. And with *wild* in his throat he saw how wrong he'd been, how false his idea to freeze the scene, lock it down, had been. Everything mattered—noise, commotion, disorder, change, yes, death too was part of what he needed to take with him. All of it. Toni *was* change and movement, had been, would be. She—*they*—never had been static. How had he not seen that? *She's going someplace,* he said to himself, *only to earth, but that's the right path.* His hunger for stasis, his avoidance—false desires, empty. She'd made the potent choice, drawing herself to him, kissing, declaring, *It's me. This is it.*

Elliot hesitated, even bent forward towards her a little, then backed to the door, turned and walked out past Alec and the nurse and went downstairs to the boys and their game. He had trouble focusing on their screen, but set them up for blood and mayhem anyway. Hoarse screaming and virtual death, magic bullets. If you had enough points you didn't have to stay dead.

In the car he realized he had said no more after *I have loved you.* The thought stayed with him all the way to Boston, *that was my goodbye,* all the way to Boston at high speed in the rain. It was a comfort to him to have left her with that, exactly that, and its acceptance.

*

When Elliot turned into the strange driveway he was surprised. Alec had called him in Boston the day after his goodbye visit to say Toni had died. He'd only given him the address and the rules she'd laid down: There would be a party at which everyone would bring flowers and a favorite dish, at which there would be waltzing. Then everyone would take someone else's flowers home. He'd thought the party would be at an ordinary house, but this was a mansion with a long driveway curving back into trees. It was packed with cars and as he drove past the entrance he could see a crowd inside. He had been thinking there would be twenty or thirty people at this party, that it would be something casual and loving, friends reminiscing, the family.

The family was in the entrance hall but after he had put down his food and flowers and hugged them and gone on into the mansion he realized there must be two hundred people. He knew no one, no one at all. Where had they all come from? Sure, it was a tight small-college community, but, but.... Could they all have been friends? It was startling to think so. Beautifully dressed smooth people—were they administrators? Students, some dressed for a party, others more casually, a sprinkling of plainly dressed natural people, and lots of kids—he spotted her two little ones—running around with balloons, spraying confetti from aerosol cans. They could have been at a New Year's Eve party.

Elliot put the flowers he'd bought in Boston on a shelf, and his food, barely warm after the long drive, on the table. He stood back against a wall and looked around. Where to start mingling? The smooth people, who if nothing else were his age? No, not them. She'd disliked administrators, but here they were anyway, claiming space, claiming her, being seen to claim her in a way he could not.

Instead, he ate. He loaded his plate with food, indiscriminately piling spoonfuls one on top of another, and took a seat at an empty table, a place facing away from the crowd, looking out a window onto Seneca Lake. Snow coming, he'd heard on the car radio, it should start soon. *Who do they think I am?* he wondered, and decided no one would be thinking anything about a middle-aged guy in wrinkled clothes, eating alone. Just another acquaintance.

Elliot couldn't help turning and looking over his shoulder, as if for a person who had been supposed to have joined him, someone who might not recognize him from the rear. He was lonely and realized he was on the verge of anger, no, not on the verge. He was angry. No one knew who he was. He resented these people—in his place—he who had sat at the deathbed! When resentment welled up in him he was ashamed.

Sitting alone, eating servings of food jammed together on a paper plate, mixed textures and flavors, the dry swimming in the wet, all a mess he thought, *but that's how it always is anyway.* Who goes to the buffet table and comes away with one or two helpings, the way food is served at a real dinner? Instead, you load your plate with everything because you don't want to have to get back in line, don't want to cut in, don't know what you're going to want until you move down the line and see it in front of you.

The thick texture of noise and warring tastes penetrated his resentment. *I'm getting it wrong again,* he thought. Sitting back, he lowered his guard, opened the gates, and let all the sensations crash in at once: the food, talk, laughter, music from the combo in the next room. Now it felt exactly like a party, one at which he belonged. Well, it *was* a party, ordered by his friend, served up after her death. And so far he had been a poor guest. He owed the friend of his heart better than this.

A young man walked through the crowd. "Waltzing at 8:30, instruction at a quarter after."

Two lines began forming near where Elliot was sitting—men in one, women in the other—so he stood up, but behind the men, not quite ready to take his place in line.

Elliot had noticed the woman earlier because of her hair. She had a wavy pulled-back mass of hair, dark and streaked with gray, a combination which had always pleased him. She was a large woman, tall and with ample breasts, which appeared to be swinging freely beneath her shirt. She seemed a comforting woman to Elliot, relaxed, so dancing with her should be easy.

The lines moved forward and met, leaving Elliot behind. Leaving the woman on the other side behind, too. He caught her eye. She raised her eyebrows at him and he nodded *Yes*, and worked his way through the couples already being instructed—*one*-two-three, *one*-two-three— to stand in front of her.

"Will you waltz with me?" he said.

"Yes. My name is Alexis."

"Mine is Elliot."

She put out her arms, and so did he, taking her right hand in his left, putting his right on her back, the standard ballroom dancing position. He hadn't forgotten that. Alexis seemed stiff, stiffer than he expected. She wasn't bending towards him. She wasn't coming into his arms. He wasn't going to envelop her in his arms and slow dance the way he'd done as a teen-ager, bodies touching, slow dancing in the gym, slow dancing because he danced so poorly, and certainly he wasn't going to dance gracefully and beautifully the way some others already were, though there was no music yet, just the dancing master's one-two-three, one-two-three, but he wanted to hold her in a way that would let them dance. And here he was with a stiff partner, a rigid one. For all that she was smiling and friendly, respectful of him, respectful of what they were doing, which of course was not slow-dancing at a high school dance but dancing a waltz for their friend who had died.

"You're not from the College," she said.

"No, I'm from Buffalo. A friend," Elliot answered, no longer wanting to reveal himself, and she let it go at that.

All Elliot's dancing had been with women who were more skilled than he, women who had carried him along—had frankly *led* him. Alexis couldn't get the box step right, which meant that Elliot couldn't, either. The whole of their dancing was less than the sum of its parts.

"I'm sorry," she said, "I'm a pretty good athlete, actually, and I should be able to dance, but I can't."

Elliot remembered an email Toni had sent after one of the bad times, one of the times she'd admitted fear and depression. *I'm ballroom dancing again, though*, she wrote, *so maybe I can waltz it all away. Let me give you some waltz words: telemark (no skis), slip pivot and banjo, swirls. Open impeti. It's doing me good.*

Alexis wouldn't move closer to him and he didn't want to pull her in. But this far apart it wasn't working. It was uncomfortable, but he wasn't sure he wanted her closer, actually, because that might seem like cheating on Toni. *Goddam*, Elliot thought as he woodenly box stepped with Alexis, one-two-three, one-two-three in the dance master's cadence, *why the hell didn't I dance with Toni?*

They could have danced together in her kitchen the brittle night she wept for her ravaged body. He could have gotten up from the table and danced with her and something would have flowed and brought back the sweetness. They would have been partners, and it wouldn't have mattered how badly he danced. She could have shown him what a telemark was, they could have slip pivoted into an open impetus, and the pup would have barked and the kids would have heard the commotion, come downstairs, and laughed at the two baldies waltzing on the old linoleum, an elbow hitting the refrigerator, a hip the washer. It might have softened and lightened the burnt sugar back into caramel.

Because Alexis wouldn't move in closer Elliot's elbow couldn't bend and couldn't crook out to make room, so his forearm was pressing the side of her breast. She didn't seem annoyed, but Elliot didn't think she could be enjoying it. He wasn't. Any other time he'd have wanted his partner closer, but he didn't want to hold Alexis in his arms, to use dancing as an excuse to hold her in his arms, this woman who would never have come into his arms under any other circumstances. Another time he'd have felt excitement and anticipation at having his arm where it was, anticipation that this woman would be in his arms in another way entirely. Any other time, but not now.

It was hard, very hard, and got no better when the music started. Alexis leaned towards him, saying they should get in the center of the floor where they wouldn't be so visible. But it was no better there for him, surrounded by couples, box-stepping woodenly near the band. And the band! It was some kind of western trio, or maybe folkies with an expanded repertoire: a bass and two guitars, playing too fast in three-fourths time.

Elliot, at arm's length, looked directly at Alexis. Their eyes met easily enough. "I'm sorry," he said, "I'm so sorry I'm not a better waltzer. But I never learned."

"Don't apologize. Neither did I."

When the dance ended Elliot made a little bow and thanked Alexis. "We did it," he said. "Thank you."

She smiled and inclined her head at him. "Thank *you*."

Elliot turned away and left the floor. *Don't look back*, he said to himself. He stood for a moment in the doorway, feeling the crowd move around him. Dancers were leaving the floor and others were entering to take their places. Motion, all motion around him, motion and noise. He edged to the side and stood against a wall, staying there a minute, watching the crowd, then—deciding abruptly, as if to hang up or log off—picked up a foil-wrapped pot of living chrysanthemums, hugged the family, got his coat and left, leaving the music inside.

It was snowing heavily, but there was no wind. The flakes, large and quiet, muffled the noise from inside. He felt them melting on his head. He heard himself breathing in, counting one-two-three, out one-two-three. His own three-fourths this time, just the cadence. No melody. Clear of the mansion, in the new snow, Elliot stepped out, turned, saw no one watching, went up on his toes and spun, stepped wide again, covering ground, flowerpot in his elbow, pressed to his chest, unexpectedly sharp, turned to see footprints, two together, one apart. Raking light from the mansion cast shadows in the ruts his dragging toes had made. Black asphalt exposed in dancer tracks, already ragged-edged in blowing snow. The bright mansion rotated by, its porte-cochere empty. He whispered towards it, *Come out, come, come out.*

Moving backwards, sideways, Elliot danced the driveway, lit by wan street lamps, their yellow globes his balloons, snow-covered trunk lids and bumpers his chairs, friend of his heart in his arms. Lazy white confetti. Elliot waltzed a shade, a shade drawn from light, took her close enough to dance, really dance, lifting his arm to spin her, grace at last with them.

David Hunter
Do Doves Really Sleep In The Sand?

"I wonder…" Johnson said, tinkering with the trigger of the shotgun mounted in the locked holder between us. I know the safety is on, but I've told him a thousand times not to do it. He's one of those dumbass college graduate cops who know everything.

"You wonder *what?*" I asked.

"Do doves really sleep in the sand?"

"I wouldn't think so. Doves nest above ground"

"I guess you've shot a lot of doves in your life," Johnson said.

"Hell no! I haven't been hunting since I got into police work. Why would you say that, Johnson?"

"Your entire generation was caught up in the macho thing. I just thought…"

"Johnson, do you own a mountain bike and spend weekends riding around in those little elastic shorts?"

"No. Why do you ask?

"Because your whole generation is into it, maybe?"

The boy grows silent and has the good grace to know he's been hoisted on his own petard. He says, "Touché."

"Why did you ask the question in the first place, rookie?"

"What question?"

"You were speculating as to whether doves actually sleep in the sand, why?"

"Oh yeah. My dad was listening to some of those old cassette tapes of his this morning. Kramer, did I ever tell you that he still had

*'I have no hobbies except
reading and writing,
which I've always viewed
as lifelong passions.'*

~ David Hunter

an old eight-track system when I was little? He still doesn't own any music on a disk."

"The eight-track tape system had excellent sound and was a lot sturdier than cassette tapes. Now, Johnson—*focus*. Why were you asking me about doves sleeping in the sand?"

I swing up Joe Lewis Road for a sweep through Monkey Village. It's a federal housing project. The real name is Montgomery Village but we've always called it Monkey Village as long as I can remember; and I remember a lot.

"Dad was playing this ancient song by Bob Dylan called "Blowin' in the Wind." There was a verse about a white dove sleeping in the sand. I just wondered if doves really sleep in the sand."

I pull up to a stop sign, turn and stare at Johnson like a stain on the rug. He's wearing some kind of Greek fraternity pin as a tie tack. I still have my old blue pig tie tack. The one that stands for "pride, integrity and guts." I've been wearing it since 1979 when I pinned on my badge.

"Bob Dylan is not fucking *ancient*, Johnson! He was still writing some of his best stuff when I was humping the boonies in 'Nam."

"That was like, what, three or four wars ago, Kramer?"

"That's FTO, *fucking Field Training Officer* Kramer to you, rookie."

I jerk away from the stop sign and it throws Johnson back, catching his finger in the trigger guard of the shotgun. He puts the knuckle in his mouth for a second.

"Geez, *FTO Kramer.* I didn't mean it as an insult. I was just trying to point out that it was a long time ago."

"Ancient is like *thousands* of years, Johnson. Not thirty or forty."

"Monkey alert!" Johnson suddenly yells. "Two of them at the end of the block prying up a storm drain cover!"

I immediately see them. Since I've been a cop, kids in this project have pried tons of storm drain grates up. They break them up, sell them to the foundry and the foundry turns them into new storm drain grates. It's killer work to break cast iron. Legitimate work is easier, but the kids keep doing it.

We bail out of the cruiser and the three kids run, two white kids and a black kid. The black kid stumbles, so I make him as my prey. Johnson is already closing on another. All these new cops lift weights at the Fraternal Order of Police gym, then go play tennis or handball.

They don't smoke, either. When I started, there would always be a layer of smoke at roll call and everyone would have a cup of coffee. These new kids drink *diet sodas*, for God's sake.

I'm actually gaining on the kid when I step on something slick—a flattened beer can maybe—and turn my ankle. I go down hard and know I've lost skin on one knee and an elbow. I'm limping back to the cruiser when Johnson comes back with a redheaded kid of sixteen or so. He's crying and Johnson isn't even winded.

"You all right, Kramer?" Johnson asks.

"Yeah, I'm fine."

"You've torn your pants. You want to transport this one to the house so you can change?"

"No. It's only a couple of hours until we go in. I've worked in clothes more ragged than this. I'll call the wagon to pick up this big-time thief."

*

I turn the cruiser loose a little as we head up Chapman Highway for a look at the far end of our beat. Of course, these new vehicles with all the gadgets for pollution control are nothing like what we used to have.

My first cruiser was a 1980 Chevelle that would pin you to the seat when you put your foot in it. The new ones drive a lot smoother though.

I spot the drift of the old Ford ahead just as the rookie says, "Drunk driver alert!"

"On my radar," I say, kicking it in the ass and closing on the old Ford. The rookie is already typing in the plate number as I hit the blues and bump the siren once. It looks like the driver may rabbit on me, but after looking in the rearview mirror a couple of times, he pulls over to the shoulder.

"Unit 2714, we'll be out behind a white ninety-one Ford—tag number GIF-321."

"It's a stolen tag," Johnson says, reading the computer screen.

"Wonder why he didn't run?" I say. "Driver, put both hands out the window where I can see them," I say over the intercom. The sound echoes off the buildings on both sides of the highway.

We open the doors and stand beside the cruiser, but I keep the microphone in my hand. "Driver, open the car door with your right hand and push it open. Keep your hands where I can see them."

The driver complies. He is short and stocky, dressed in blue jeans and a long-sleeved denim shirt. Thirty, maybe thirty-five years old. He looks more disgusted than scared.

"Put your hands behind your head, driver. Walk backwards towards us. Do it now!"

The man complies and I drop the mike in the seat. A proper felony technique would be to put him face downward on the ground, but there are two of us, we have good light, and I decide to cut a corner. I know better, but I do it anyway.

With my Glock .40-caliber by my leg, I approach the man. Johnson is moving parallel with me, his weapon slightly raised. Rookies are good and scared. That's the way it should be.

When we are in place, I slide my pistol back into the holster and do a quick pat down of our man—beginning under the arms, sliding down to the belt, reaching around in the front, then down the outside of his legs and up the inside to the groin area. No lumps or bulges.

"Now, keep your hands behind your head. I'm going to move you against the car. Do exactly what I tell you. Understand, my friend?"

"Yeah." The man has a deep voice. He still appears more bored than anything else.

Grabbing his hands and gripping them tightly, I take his belt in the other hand and move him to the side of his old Ford. I kick his legs apart and back like I've done a thousand times before. Then things unwind.

The man suddenly drops to a crouch at the same moment I hear something whistle past my ear. The man screams as there is a sound like kindling wood breaking.

The sound is from the shattered bone in his wrist. The whistling from the collapsible baton Johnson carries. I still have an old PR-24 baton because it has served me well for thirty-five years.

As the man whimpers and groans, his face against the side of his car, I see the knife I missed in his sleeve when I patted him down. It's on the ground beside him and Johnson picks it up.

It's what we used to call a "Black Beauty" when I was a rookie. The blade is spring-loaded in the grip and pops out at the touch of a button. Johnson has probably never seen one. I have two or three in my collection at home.

"Good work, Johnson," I say through a dry mouth. Later I will find that the man we stopped had a parole violation and enough warrants to send him back to the walls for the rest of his life. Apparently he just wanted to kill a cop before he went back. I had drawn the black ball this time around.

I take the prisoner back to the cruiser and cuff him to the rear door handle to wait for the ambulance my partner is calling and I feel bad about the way I treated the rookie.

I remember when I first went out, how the remaining Korean War vets and the occasional World War II vet made fun of my associates degree in criminal justice and my time as a military police officer. I hadn't thought about it in a long time.

Within five minutes, a supervisor, an ambulance and a television crew have arrived. I stay out of the way and let the supervisor and the rookie talk to the cameras. I've talked to more cameras than I care to remember. It's Johnson's collar. He deserves it. I've decided to put him in for a commendation.

*

We are an hour past shift change as we head into the house. Paperwork takes a lot of time. I plan to get Johnson into the station soon enough to see himself interviewed on the six o'clock news. It will be his first time.

He is drinking a diet cola that some civilian brought him at the scene. I'm sipping a cold cup of coffee I got myself from a market across the street. He seems pleased with himself and should be.

"Officer Johnson?"

He seems startled. I've never called him *officer* before. "Yes, FTO Kramer?"

"Doves *don't* sleep in the sand. Bob Dylan was a good poet and songwriter, but he didn't know dick about doves. His real name was Robert Zimmerman.

"He was a city boy from Duluth, Minnesota who wanted to be like a guy named Woody Guthrie. He just needed a word that rhymed with *man* when he was writing 'Blowing in the Wind.' He used 'sleeps in the sand.'"

"You seem to know a lot about him," Johnson says.

"He's not much older than I am and there was a time when I wanted to be a musician, just like Dylan."

"What happened?" Johnson asked.

"I took a graduation trip to Vietnam and then life happened."

"All I ever wanted to be was a cop," Johnson says. "I was lucky, I guess."

"Talk to me in twenty years and let me know if you change your mind."

"I'll do that."

I can tell he's humoring me, though. I'm almost sixty. Today he saved my life from a stupid, rookie mistake. In twenty years, if I live that long, I'll be nearly eighty. And who gives a damn about what an eighty-year-old ex-cop thinks, anyway?

Cathy Kodra

The Most Interesting Thing in the World

*A*t the airport, Pearl sat and watched people go by. It was the best watching place, she found, because it was safe. Plenty of uniformed guards and no riff-raff. Riff-raff couldn't afford airline tickets.

The people, although decidedly not poor, were eccentric and varied enough to suit her. Tall, short, slim, stocky, fat, beyond fat, obese. Pretty, glamorous, ugly, bland, acne-pocked, clear-skinned, wart-infested, painted, tattooed, scarred, burned, pierced, birth-marked. Elated, broken-hearted, everything in between.

She loved the impersonal banality of watching people walk past. Saturdays were airport days for Pearl, and except for the faces, nothing much changed. Until one particular Saturday, when two startling events occurred—one minor, involving a rat, and one major, involving a man—and everything changed.

Pearl couldn't understand why people watched TV, except maybe for the History Channel, or when it was raining hard, pouring buckets outside, windows streaming, no visibility even with binoculars, maybe then you'd stay inside in front of the television with a nice glass of White Zinfandel. But here in Flynn, Tennessee, it was only seventeen miles to the sixteen-gate Flynn Memorial Airport. It wasn't an international airport, granted, but enough people of different races, ethnic groups, abilities, and disabilities passed through to keep her well satisfied.

On Saturday mornings, Pearl packed a huge, blue quilted tote bag with a neatly folded sweater, a notebook, five carefully-sharpened pencils, six Snickers bars, aloe lip balm, a comb, a mirror, chewing

'To become a better writer, read, read, and read some more. Read the writers you and others admire the most and those who are respected award-winning authors. Read books about writing; make it a daily study and a part of your scheduled writing time. Carry a notebook everywhere. Write.'

~ Cathy Kodra

gum, her wallet, and a few of her favorite blue ink pens (she wouldn't write with black ink—too stuffy and official looking, verging on mean) and headed out Route 27 to Flynn Memorial. She could have taken the interstate, but all those whizzing cars and angry drivers scared her half to death. Route 27 was civilized. There were gas stations and convenience stores if you broke down or got hungry. She always pocketed a little cash, left her wallet in the glove compartment of her charcoal-gray Toyota, parked in short term, walked up the ramp to the lower level baggage claim area, cheerfully and resolutely marched her smallish, wiry frame through the massive, automatic double doors and announced to no one in particular that she was meeting her grandson, who was flying in from Dallas. Or her niece from San Antonio, or her cousin from Sacramento. She kept the cities large enough and far enough away in case anyone asked her questions. No one ever did.

Pearl didn't know if any of her immediate family still existed, and she didn't want to know. Her Aunt Harriet had written years ago when Pearl's father died, and then again two years after that when her mother died. Pearl never answered either letter or made any attempt to go back north for the funerals. In fact, Pearl had grown weary of people close up, and she didn't like pets much, either. She liked birds and other animals from a distance but had never hoped to own any. She hung birdfeeders in her yard, lay carrots and bits of lettuce along her wooden privacy fence for the neighborhood rabbits, put out trays of dry cat food for the feral cats that roamed the woods behind her little bungalow, and gave an entire one-third of her yearly income—pension and Social Security combined—to the local food pantry. Pearl believed people should work for a living and earn their way in this world. She certainly had. Forty-eight years of nursing home and factory work. Nevertheless, she couldn't stomach the idea of anyone, anywhere, for any reason, including laziness, starving to death. Not even prisoners. Not even captors. Not animals, not vermin. Pearl knew what it meant to be hungry.

Her parents, poor as church mice, had sometimes made Pearl and her three brothers and two sisters rotate meals based on the days of the week. Mondays, Wednesdays, and Fridays belonged to the boys. Tuesdays, Thursdays, and Saturdays were for the girls. If you were good. Sunday everyone got to eat, although that wasn't much of a bonus. Her mother had learned to stretch any little scrap of food into a meal, and Sunday was definitely scrap day. The days you didn't get a meal you might get two pieces of stale bread and a stomachache. Once, Pearl had gone six days without anything to eat. She couldn't remember if her siblings had done the same, but she supposed they had. Lucky for all of them that two of her mother's babies had been stillborn.

Born and raised in Chapman, New York, thirty-five miles south of the Canadian border, Pearl knew that her family wasn't the only starving family around. She knew kids at school, when she went to school, who stole food daily just to survive. Chapman was a windy, flat, dying town with ignorant, poor people who spawned ignorant, poor offspring. The population had never reached five hundred in all her years of growing up there, even counting the Mohawk Indian reservation five miles down the road. Chapman boasted a general store, a post office on the enclosed front porch of a Miss Amy Graham's house, a tiny Methodist church, and large fields of cows and corn. The children all walked to the school in the next town west of Chapman, that is, when the roads were plowed and no one was sick. Pearl couldn't seem to remember a time when the roads were clear and no one was sick. If there was such a time, it was when school was out, and it was summer. In summer, Pearl had stolen every spare minute away from washing dishes, doing laundry, mopping floors, helping with the haying, and feeding and milking three failing cows.

High up in the hayloft with her nose in a book, she read anything and everything she could get her hands on (her parents only had five books counting the Bible), and the ones she loved best were *The Wind in the Willows* and *The Last of the Mohicans*, both of which she read for the first time at age nine, and with equal devotion.

As a young woman, Pearl had become fascinated with starvation. She followed every piece of news regarding the fate of the European Jews during the war, and years later she read everything she could get her hands on about what happened in Germany and Poland. Elie Wiesel was her favorite author, but she read everything else she could find—nonfiction, fiction, and poetry. When the librarian in Flynn asked if she was of Jewish descent, Pearl said, "Yes, in a way." The librarian stared at her strangely, and Pearl hurried off, another book about the Holocaust tucked under her arm. They were comforting, those books. Other little girls had been hungry. Other children had been much worse off than she.

The airport was safe. No one there ever appeared to be starving. No one had the gnawing pain, the broken nails, dull brittle hair, fragile bones, waning skin turgor, open sores, haunted eyes as empty as the stomach, the rage, the hopelessness, and finally the desperate cunning—a willingness to harm another for a crust of stale bread or part of a rotten apple. Because one could become obsessed, even possessed, one might trade the dark-haired girl child spared at birth for a cupful of weak onion broth. One would. It could not be denied.

Pearl would be seventy-eight in April. She was lean and strong for a woman her age. She ate voraciously, her birdlike eyes darting quickly this way and that, her mouth working in tiny, abbreviated thrusts that stopped on a dime if anyone met her eyes. A small halo of white hair quivered faintly with each thrust. She preferred to dine alone; in fact, she insisted on it. At the airport, she had a favorite restroom with a plaque on the door that read *Employees Only*. It contained a single sink with a mirror, one toilet, a narrow broom closet, and two locks on the door, one a button lock on the knob and the other a bolt. When she ate her Snickers bars or any additional snacks she purchased from the vending machines, that was where she went, safely locked in and cozy. And it was clean, usually. Sometimes, when the cleaning crew was too busy, stains appeared in the sink or a faint ring formed in the toilet bowl. Then Pearl would open the closet and remove a bucket, spray cleaner, and rag and go to town on the toilet and sink. There never was any Windex to be found, so she cleaned the mirror with the rag and clear water.

Sometimes the cleaning people would be nearby when she came

out, but they had long ago stopped giving her warning looks and trying to guide her to the public restrooms. Only once, in the beginning, had anyone threatened to call security. That threat had been delivered in faltering English by a young Mexican man, but the older cleaning lady with him, also Mexican, had spoken rapidly and angrily in Spanish and no guard had appeared. At least not before Pearl made her hasty exit. Perhaps the cleaning woman found the candy wrappers in the restroom trashcan and understood. Or perhaps she was just kind. Or maybe it was the twenty-dollar bill Pearl tucked into the metal ring of the toilet paper holder at the end of each airport visit. The cleaning people always watched her until she was almost out of sight down the long corridor that led away from the security checkpoint for Gates 1 through 8, and Pearl always looked back just in time to see the petite, solemn Hispanic woman dart inside the restroom to retrieve the twenty. Of course, occasionally she wasn't working that day and someone else got the bill, but Pearl liked her best, and she usually worked Saturdays, so it mostly came out fine. The woman was thin, and Pearl hoped she spent the money on food. Most Mexicans weren't so thin, were they? Pearl didn't think so.

*

Hunger was the most interesting thing in the world. Also the most terrifying and unforgiving. Hunger was more dangerous than nuclear weapons or holes in the ozone layer or poisonous snakes or leprosy or driving on the interstate. Hunger made people commit horrible, evil acts. Even poor old Eva was not as afraid as she was hungry, at least at one point.

Eva had been placed on the skilled wing of the nursing home, not the residential wing. That meant Eva was very sick, disabled, or dangerous to others or herself. When Pearl started working at Rainbow Haven, she worked residential for the first month. Verna would wander the corridor late at night, asking if anyone knew what street she lived on or where her house was, because she had forgotten. Roger masturbated nightly in his room, the door and his pebbly little black eyes wide open, his right leg and the stub of the left one braced firmly against the bleached sheets on his bed. Jennie, ninety-four, still painted charming pictures of the Holston River with the watercolors her niece brought her, but she grew increasingly tired and wanted only to remember the paintings she created in the past.

They were a little strange, some of these patients, but they were residential. They could wash themselves, feed themselves, and go to the bathroom mostly unassisted. Pearl put a sign up on Verna's door that read "Verna's House." She gave Roger an extra blanket and told him to shut the door and cover up, for God's sake. And she listened to Jennie's vivid descriptions of her artwork from thirty years ago, getting to the point in the monologue where Pearl had a burning question about a particular painting, only to find Jennie napping in the middle of a sentence.

One night at ten forty-five, Eva Friedman flipped her lid. Or had "another psychotic episode," as the doctor on call would write in his notes. Pearl always remembered the exact time because it was shift change, and none of the nurses or nurses' aides wanted to help a living soul if it meant five minutes of extra duty past their shift. Pearl was ordered to meet the supervising RN in Eva's room over on the skilled side since they were short on aides that night.

The nursing home was a large square with roughly half the square housing residential patients and the other half skilled patients, skilled meaning they had little or no skills, if you looked at it truthfully.

Pearl, not against panning for a little overtime pay, had willingly hurried over to Room 17 where the evening nurse was kneeling on the edge of the bed nearest the door, her hands wedged between old, bony knees, carefully delivering a doll from the depths of Eva's dry, shriveled vagina. Eva was howling, "The baby, the baby, please don't take my baby!" in her heavy German accent. Pearl stood there, perplexed, until the nurse turned slightly toward her and asked would she like to help or get the hell out and go home? Pearl asked what she should do and was told to get a washcloth and towel to bathe the baby and a blanket to wrap it in. Couldn't she see there was a baby being born here?

That was her first meeting with Eva, and the staff on skilled told Pearl what little they knew of Eva's story: a concentration camp in Germany in the early forties, a child taken from her at birth, no surviving family members, no knowledge of the baby's father. That same night, when Eva finally rested comfortably in the arms of Haldol, a tranquilizer used more often at Rainbow Haven than seemed safe, Pearl slipped back into Eva's room. She walked around the bed to the side facing the windows and sat gently on the edge of the mattress. She had clocked out after the birthing enactment and a short discussion with the supervising nurse, and now she could hear the crests and troughs of garbled conversation flowing from the staff meeting room down the hall. The three other patients in Eva's room were snoring, mumbling, and making various sleep-induced sounds in their respective corners. Pearl knew that the woman in the bed diagonal from Eva's had undergone a partial lobotomy for brain cancer before being admitted, but she hadn't yet been able to bring herself to stand beside the woman's bed to see that caved-in skull.

Moonlight streamed through the windows on the back wall of the room, its pale sheen spilling across white sheets on the bed parallel to Eva's and onto Eva's craggy profile. Pearl noted the way the light glowed within Eva's pendulous left earlobe and then passed through it, how it rippled on the folds of her wrinkled neck. She leaned over and inhaled, pulling the sour smell of aging flesh, mingled with scents of baby powder and lemon glycerin, deep into her lungs. She watched Eva's frail chest expand and deflate slowly, treacherously. Pearl laid her left hand lightly over the left side of this chest and imagined she felt Eva's old, worn heart tapping faintly but steadily.

In a quick, stealthy swoop, Pearl bent down and unlaced her white shoes, pushing them off one at a time, and gently swung her feet up onto the narrow cot, settling her own small body next to Eva's. Pearl balanced cautiously because she was off the bed as much as she was on it. The side that was half-on sensed the slight warmth from Eva's limp frame. Pearl turned her head and watched the moon, feeling a contentment she'd not known before. She stayed, motionless, listening to Eva's slow breaths until they were drowned by the swell of voices coming through the now-open door down the hall. The aides would be around on Changes shortly, checking bed sores, turning patients, and changing soiled sheets.

Pearl left the bed, donning her shoes and gliding away down the hall, beyond the far corner, and through ponderous double doors into the bracing night air.

The very next morning, Pearl marched down the hall to the director's office and asked to be transferred to third shift on the skilled side of Rainbow Haven. Pleasantly surprised and not one to squander an advantageous request, the director of nursing promptly obliged.

Thus started Pearl's long acquaintance with Eva and many nights of delivering the doll, hiding the doll, promising to hold and protect the doll, and bringing the doll back to Eva for clandestine visits. Pearl loved to talk to Eva, to comfort her, to try to get her to eat.

One night Eva was parked out at the nurses' station, a member of a half circle of Geri chairs filled with residents eating their bland dinners. A young aide was attempting to feed a reluctant Eva—a gaunt, bony, undernourished Eva.

"Come on, Eva," the impatient aide muttered. "You need to eat." On each upward swing of the fork, the aide repeated this mantra in the same singsong voice. "You need to eat. You're getting thin. You need some healthy food."

Pearl stood watching from the end of the nearest corridor, and she saw Eva's face get the stubborn, scared look that forecast an outburst—the down-turned lip, the faint scowl. She knew Eva well enough by now to know that she was suspicious of the food, hungry but angry, and you could only push her so far. Just as Pearl edged forward to signal the aide who was chanting *You need to eat* one final time, Eva swung a long arm forward, knocked the fork out of the aide's hand, mashed potatoes flying into the unsuspecting girl's blonde bangs, and yelled in her guttural, surprisingly deep voice:

"I'll tell you what I need! I need a good stiff cock, that's what I need! Now get the hell away from me!"

The aide hurried off, brushing futilely at the potatoes stuck in her hair, crying and cursing under her breath. Another aide moved in quickly and started wheeling Eva toward her room as an elderly man in the semicircle brought trembling hands up from his lap and applauded weakly three times, a thin smile tracing his lips. His name was Alvin, and he could often be seen stark naked, wandering the corridors and insisting to any scolding nurse that he was indeed wearing clothes. He had ruined one large section of orange carpet next to an emergency exit with his nightly habit of pissing in only that particular spot. His lovely, sane wife came every single day of the year to help care for him. She treated him tenderly and lovingly, even when he tried to pinch the nurses' behinds. *He never used to be that way*, she'd explain to the staff each time it happened, as if they wouldn't understand.

Pearl quickly grew protective of Eva during those months on the skilled side, and she watched and waited for signs of improvement. She wanted Eva to be well, to understand that the war was over, that her baby was no longer in danger. At the very least, she wanted Eva to trust her, to allow Pearl to feed her, but that was not to be. Eva was suspicious and irrevocably damaged by history.

Once, on one of the last nights that Pearl took care of her, Eva motioned Pearl to her bedside, a sly grin touching her old, trembling lips.

"Take the baby, she's yours," Eva whispered. "Just bring me a cup of broth with a little meat, and you can have her." Her yellow teeth broke free of the lips for a moment, forming a hideous, malevolent sneer.

Pearl collapsed on the edge of Eva's bed and sobbed, unhinged, and the head nurse on skilled told her later the same night that she was too emotionally invested to work in a nursing home. Three days later, Eva died in her sleep, the doll clamped between her knees. Pearl turned in her keys and a hastily scrawled resignation and never looked back. For the rest of her working years, she remained anonymous and detached, on one assembly line or another.

*

This particular Saturday was cool, the sky filled with dark streaks of cirrus clouds, the air soft with autumn moisture. Pearl loved the way southern air felt on her skin. It made it feel supple, younger. She never missed the cold, dry air of Chapman or the flat farmland; she'd not been back in years. Flynn had been home for a long time now. It reminded her of the Adirondacks far south of Chapman, the beautiful blue-tinged mountains that cradled clear lakes and small, carefully tended communities between Plattsburgh and Albany.

Stepping briskly off the edge of the patio, she made her way out to the clothesline, a white rope stretched between two oaks in the backyard. She took down a pair of jeans and her gray sweater, tucking clothespins into the pocket of her flowered housedress, humming to herself. Pearl brought the clothes back to the patio and draped them over a lawn chair. Picking up two plastic buckets, she made her way around the perimeter of the yard, dropping morsels of food along the fence and filling empty aluminum trays with dry cat food. There was no need to leave water; the little creek behind her fence was full this October thanks to the abundance of rain. She stopped to watch a cardinal at the base of one of her feeders; he was picking his way through oak leaves to find fallen sunflower seeds. Pearl appreciated the redness of him this early in the day, and it cheered her to see him eating so determinedly.

An hour later, after biscuits and mint tea, Pearl was on the road to the airport. She felt hesitant today and didn't know why. Maybe it wasn't a good day to go. Her stomach was unsettled—the mint tea hadn't agreed with her this morning. She couldn't imagine what else she'd do on a Saturday, however, so she drove on, never topping forty-five miles an hour.

When Pearl reached Flynn Memorial, there was an ambulance parked outside. *Not good*, she thought. Maybe there had been an accident or someone had a heart attack. She hoped it wasn't Petra, for by now she knew the Mexican custodian's name. She had glimpsed her nametag two visits ago. It wasn't intentional, as Pearl didn't particularly *want* to know her name. It would be best if she didn't know the woman's name, she felt. There needn't be any familiarity between them.

Shuffling tentatively toward the double doors, Pearl sniffed the air. Sometimes she could smell things other people couldn't. Sometimes she really could smell danger, although she knew it was only a saying. Danger smelled metallic, though it wasn't worth telling anyone that. They'd just think she was crazy.

A furtive movement caught her eye to the left of the entryway, a grayish-brown streak that scurried behind a trash container. She stopped and then saw the rat slinking toward a piece of bagel nearby on the sidewalk, bright, beady eyes taking in her presence. Suddenly, the rat darted across the concrete directly to Pearl, and lightly, ever so lightly, touched the tip of his nose to the toe of her black sneaker. Then he was off, tugging at the morsel of bread that was half as big as he was, gradually pulling it safely into the space behind the garbage bin. *Amazing*, thought Pearl. She actually saw a whisker brush the material of her sneaker. Never particularly afraid of mice or rats, for they had been frequent residents in the barn of her childhood, she had remained stock still while it checked her shoe. Perhaps the sneaker smelled of some sort of food. Maybe she'd stepped on something edible while crossing from short-term parking to the entry of the airport. Still, it was bold. She'd never seen any rodents around the airport before, inside or out. This was certainly a first! A few people wheeled luggage past Pearl and the rat as it all happened, but no one seemed to notice a thing.

"Eat, then," Pearl said under her breath. "Eat, little one." She felt a sudden wave of nausea and truly regretted the mint tea.

*

When Richard, the hired hand from Quebec, came into the barn that night, the metallic smell hung in the air alongside the sweet smell of hay. When he moved toward where Pearl stood in the stanchion with the pregnant cow, she had smelled it, and she'd moved backwards so quickly she fell into the hay under the cow's big triangle of a head. The man moved even quicker, unbuttoning the straps of his overalls, dropping them, and pinning her against the hay, pulling her skirt up and her panties down in one swooping motion as though he had done this a hundred times before. He snarled something in French and then thrust himself inside her. She remembered worrying that the cow would panic and step on them, but it never did. It chewed and watched them curiously, nothing more. Minutes later there was blood in the hay beneath her and her stomach was cramping, but otherwise you'd never know anything strange had happened.

The next morning, Richard and his bundle of clothes were gone. She never learned his last name; he was just Richard around the farm. Pearl didn't dare tell her mother or father because there was always the chance that this was something punishable by taking away her portion of food, or by a severe whipping, or both. Her backside already smarted from being bounced into the hard floor under the hay. Besides, what was there to tell? She could hardly describe what had happened. She was only eleven and not good at describing things she didn't understand. She thought it was probably shameful and best left unsaid as were many things in the confusing world of Chapman, New York. She simply wiped the blood away with a cloth hanging nearby on a nail, hid the cloth under a mound of hay in the corner, pulled her panties back up, and continued tending to the cow.

*

Pearl headed toward the escalator where paramedics were assisting an elderly Asian woman who apparently had tried to ride up the moving stairs carrying two cumbersome-looking bags. She was sitting on an escalator step, now stationary, and rubbing her ankle. One of the paramedics squatted by her side while the other stuffed clothes back into the bag that had opened and spilled its contents. Pearl was glad, not that the woman was hurt, but that it wasn't serious and that Petra was okay after all.

Pearl detoured to the left, took the elevator to the second floor, and hurried over to the rocking chairs that lined the hall leading to the checkpoint for Gates 1 through 8. She had seen nothing to justify the faint metallic smell that greeted her nostrils once inside the building, nothing other than the Asian woman's mishap. Despite being a senior citizen, Pearl hadn't lost any of her sense of smell as far as she could determine. Anyway, the scent was already starting to fade, and it wasn't *always* a sign of danger. Its memory was replaced by Starbucks coffee brewing nearby and competing with the marvelous aromas of warm, soft pretzels and bacon. Her stomach rumbled, and she thought she might make a trip to the restroom earlier than usual.

A corner of Pearl's brain noted the man with the cane who also always came here on Saturdays. He was sitting on a bench a little farther along the corridor, next to a potted plant that partially concealed his upper body. He looked to be about sixty-five, balding, an unremarkable face, really, and he usually wore a plaid shirt of one color scheme or another, as he did today. Hunter's red plaid. She never saw him walk, so she didn't know whether he truly needed the cane or not. It might simply be a prop to garner sympathy. Maybe he sat at the airport on other days, too. At first it had made her a bit nervous, his presence in the corridor each time, and he apparently not flying anywhere or meeting anyone, but he never seemed to take note of *her*, so eventually she gave him the same recognition she afforded the large *Schefflera* plants stationed by alternate windows. She chose a rocker now and dragged it slightly aside so that she was angled toward people approaching the gates. She plopped her blue bag into her lap, pulling out the gray cardigan and settling it onto her old shoulders. Glancing up after she yanked it closer around her sides—airports were the chilliest places, their only drawback—she saw Ned coming toward her, pulling a bottle of beer from the deep side pocket of his denim overalls. He carried no luggage, she noticed. She wasn't especially surprised to see him, even though he'd been dead for almost thirty years.

*

They met when she was nineteen and dying to leave the farm. He worked for her father briefly, and then one night after all the work was done, Ned and Pearl just walked away. She didn't suspect her parents had minded too much. They still had younger children to feed, although by then the farm was doing some better with twenty-five head of Holstein cows, one bull, pigs, chickens, and two fine-looking roosters. Ned had a ruddy, good-natured face, and he liked her cooking. She fed him well, and he wasn't as rough as the hired hand had been. And he spoke English. Pearl wanted babies and a house of her own. Babies she could love and feed, who would never go hungry.

Ned could give her all that. They walked the entire way to Ellenburg Depot, and then hitched a ride in the back of a truck down the turnpike to Plattsburgh where, within two days after the civil ceremony, Ned had arranged a ride to Albany with a man who had business down there. Ned promised her a proper engagement ring as soon as they got settled in Albany. The wedding ring itself was nicked and dull; she didn't know where he got it, but she didn't want to complain.

They stayed in Albany for over a year. Ned worked for a dairy farmer just outside the city, riding back and forth daily with two other men, and Pearl took in wash and sold her pies and bread to the store underneath the room they rented. Soon it was clear that something was wrong with one of them, because her curse never ceased, month after month. She grew to hate the little room over the store, with its small stove and bed shoved up against the wall. She began to complain to Ned in subtle ways, then soon in overt ways, until finally he gave in and said they could move. Where to, she had wondered, and he told her he had a cousin in Tennessee, north of Knoxville. She thought he acted a bit odd, but he said they could stay with this cousin.

"What's his name?" Pearl asked.

"What'n the hell difference does it make?" he'd answered, and Pearl let it go at that, because lately Ned had shown another side to his good-natured countenance. He drank after work—he didn't tell her, but she could smell it on him when he came up the stairs and into the stuffy, drab room. He didn't want sex as often anymore, and she suspected he saw other women. Sometimes she caught a light scent of perfume underneath the pervasive odor of manure.

One night she asked about the engagement ring he'd promised, and he said, "A woman like you don't need no engagement ring," grinning cruelly at her crestfallen look. Pearl cried a few tears, but the next morning she started plotting. She hid a little money aside each time she sold a pie or washed and ironed other people's clothes. Not enough so he'd notice, but enough to buy a bus ticket and some food to hold her over a day or two. She wrote to her family and told them she and Ned were moving to Tennessee. It was the second letter she'd written home. The first brought a short note from her mother. All it said was, *Well, you've made your bed. All the best, Ma and Dad. P.S. Please don't ever send for money. You know we don't have it.*

The second letter never elicited any response, but Pearl thought maybe they answered and she never got it. After all, she moved rather suddenly and didn't leave a forwarding address for lack of having one.

Later on she wrote from Flynn, but nobody ever replied. She told her mother in that letter that she was a divorced woman, but it wasn't so. She couldn't afford a divorce, and she didn't know if a judge would grant her one, so she pretended it was true and after enough years it felt true.

Two weeks, six hours, and thirty-seven minutes before she was going to pack up her few things, lock the door, and place her note to Ned under the doormat next to the key (for she had it planned to the minute when she would leave him), Pearl got her own surprise. Ned left her instead. He didn't show up for two nights in a row, which wasn't that unusual anymore. Sometimes he stayed over at the farm. He got sick of traveling back and forth, he told her. By the third day, though, a Friday, she was worried about a farm accident. He did run the tractor sometimes, and it was haying season. Saturday was a workday for him, Sunday being the only day off, so Saturday morning Pearl made the bed and did their own wash and hung it out back of the store on the little clothesline the landlady, Mrs. Brantham, let them share. After climbing back up to the room to fix her hair and look presentable, she headed down the steep, dark stairway again to ask Mrs. Brantham, who also ran the store and bought Pearl's baked goods, if she could beg a ride out to the farm where Ned worked, as he'd turned up missing. Pearl was practicing her little speech about how he might be hurt or dead, and how she'd bake a week's worth of pies and bread in payment, when the door at the bottom of the stairs opened, letting in a shaft of bright light and the two men Ned rode to the farm with.

"Pearl?" The taller one squinted up at her.

"Oh, Lord, he's dead?"

"No, ma'am. He done run away. Nobody's seen hide nor hair of him for three days now. He asked for an advance on his pay, and Mr. Dobbs, he obliged. Ned told him you was in the family way and needed a doctor's care."

"It's a lie." Pearl sank to the stairs. "It's a damn lie."

They asked if they could do anything, and Pearl said no. Then she thought for a moment and asked where Ned had gone off to, if they didn't mind saying.

Again the tall one spoke, the other keeping his eyes down for most of the conversation. "We heard he ran off to Cobleskill with... well, maybe with a certain woman. I'm sorry to be the one to tell you this..."

Pearl had smiled a thin, tired smile full of the past months. "Don't you worry about me. It was good of you to come let me know."

Some years later, Mrs. Brantham would send Pearl the newspaper clipping from Albany, announcing the death and listing no next of kin. The obituary said the cause of death was a bull that pinned Ned to the fence he was mending, crushing his internal organs.

*

As the man with the beer walked closer, Pearl realized it wasn't Ned, not by a long shot. Ned would be far more stooped by now, and this man didn't have Ned's red face and beefy arms. This one was darker complected, and as she examined him more carefully, she noticed that the bottle in his right hand was not a bottle at all, but a pipe wrench. *A pipe wrench.* And the man was not in a custodial uniform like Petra's, nor was he wearing a security uniform. Pearl was very familiar with the security uniforms—navy blue pants with crisp white shirts that displayed blue patches on both shoulders and a yellow emblem over the heart. The upper middle backs of the shirts said **TSA** in large, bold letters. Those shirts made Pearl feel safe.

Pearl was momentarily confused. In the background, a familiar man's voice droned, *...Please do not leave luggage unattended at any time... report any unattended baggage or suspicious behavior to airport security immediately...* and at first Pearl thought the voice belonged to the pipe wrench man, or Ned. But Ned was dead, wasn't he? The pipe wrench man had Ned's eyes, and for a moment Pearl's eyes locked with his as he swung his lowered head from side to side furtively. She saw it then, that same meanness, that disregard for others. She felt a bit foggy, and there was quite suddenly a hard, painful knot in the middle of her chest, and she tried to shout some-thing, a warning—she didn't know exactly what—but she needed to warn someone. The only sound that escaped her lips was a pitiful squeak. The last thing Pearl noticed as the space around her faded to dark was that other people were finally starting to run.

*

The small-boned, Hispanic custodian found the tan notebook right where the old lady had been slumped over like a sack of potatoes when they packed her up on a stretcher and took her away. Right after another custodian assisted the guy with the cane into a wheelchair and whisked him out of the corridor, and shortly after the man with the pipe wrench was cuffed, read his rights, and taken to be interrogated. The next day he was on the five o'clock news, telling how he was innocent, just a plumber trying to help out, trying to get a job at the airport. No one would give him a job, he complained. He was dark skinned and mistaken for Middle Eastern, but it finally came out that he was Cherokee. He was taken to Scott County Medical Center and placed in the small psychiatric ward. The only thing revealed in the news after that was that he was an alcoholic and malnourished.

Curious about what an old woman who stashed twenty dollar bills in an employee bathroom might write, the custodian took the tan notebook home to her daughter and asked her to read it out loud, translating to Spanish. The daughter read the first twelve pages, seven of which held the brief beginnings of letters to the woman's mother, written in blue ink and apparently never finished and mailed, and five of which contained grocery lists in pencil. Long lists, three columns per page, of all kinds of vegetables, meats, fruits, beans, desserts— almost any food one could imagine. When the daughter informed her mother, still in her airport uniform, that the remaining dozens of pages contained only more grocery lists, the custodian said she could throw the notebook away. It didn't seem important enough to return to the old woman, and who knew where she was anyway, or if she was even alive. Who could know anything about such eccentric people?

New Millennium Writings

Is pleased to present the New Millennium

Nonfiction Awards

Winning entries appear on pages 103-138 (see Contents pages)

Summer 2007
Britton Gildersleeve, Tulsa, OK, *Anomie*
M. Garrett Bauman, Nunda, NY, *Snake Dreams*

Winter 2007-08
Ralph Ryan, Redding, CA, *Wildfire, Hellfire*
Mil Norman-Risch, Richmond, VA, *The Day My Son Died*

HONORABLE MENTIONS

Summer 2007	*Winter 2007-08*
Joni Bour, Florence, OR	Connie Albrizio, Windsor, CT
Judilyn Brown, Philadelphia, PA	Rosalind Brenner, East Hampton, NY
Tessa Dratt, Chicago, IL	Stephanie Cassatly, Jupiter, FL
Margot Fortunato, Galt, St. Paul, MN	Annie Dawid, Westcliffe, CO
Jeff Gibbs, Somerville, MA	Martha Grace Duncan, Atlanta, GA
Cathryn Hankla, Roanoke, VA	Mellissa Gayne, Portland, OR
Eli Hastings, Seattle, WA	Ellen Graf, Cropseyville, NY
Emily Hipchen, Carrollton, GA	Gilda Haber, Silver Spring, MD
Angela Hunt, Huntington,WV	Caroline E. Heller, Roslindale, MA
Thomas Ireland, Santa Fe, NM	Julia P. Henshaw, South Lyon, MI
Bernie Libster, Hasbrouck Heights, NJ	Gail Wilson Kenna, Wicomico Church, VA
Lynn Lurie, New York, NY	Elsie Knoke, Oak Ridge, TN
Sheila MacAvoy, Santa Barbara, CA	Ellen Newberry, Santa Cruz, CA
Judith Minor, West Hollywood, CA	George Newtown, Benton, LA
Steven Rosen, West Hollywood, CA	Christine Parkhurst, Knoxville, TN
Adrienne Scherger, Syracuse, NY	Marjorie Price, New York, NY
Gail Shafarman, Oakland, CA	Diana M. Raab, Santa Barbara,CA
Harrison Solow, Lampeter, Ceredigion, UK	Laura Rose, Southampton, PA
Sergio Troncoso, New York, NY	Art Schwartz, Rockville Centre, NY
Amy Weaver, Boulder Creek, CA	Anna Sochocky, Minneapolis, MN

For guidelines to our next contest, see page 9

M. Garrett Bauman
Snake Dreaming

Speculations on Human and Reptile Consciousness

*T*he Associated Press recently reported that a man from Yocolt, Washington, who had captured a rattlesnake in Arizona was showing off his new pet to friends by kissing its mouth. "I do it all the time," he declared—just before the rattler bit his lip and nearly killed him.

Another man, bragging on his website that he trained his cobra to spit venom more accurately by holding up pencils as targets, admitted it once spat in his eye. If not for two paramedics being present during this demonstration, he probably would have been blinded. As it was, his eye swelled shut for nearly two weeks. He discounted this as an unlucky accident and continued to hold up pencils as targets.

There is more than idiocy in these stories. A man I know drapes his fifteen-foot python that can easily choke him around his neck. I've been with a hiker who leaped into knee-high grass to catch a green racer and drip it from hand to hand like a Slinky toy. Sure, they seem confident and make the rest of us look weak-kneed, but these people have an unnatural glint in their eyes. They know they're playing with fire. I don't hate snakes. Far from it. But I have a complex relationship with them. We all do—whether we know it or not.

Once I accidentally ran over a small, ring-necked snake with a lawnmower. The mangled animal thrashed wildly, and I felt a sickening pang as I considered how to end the creature's misery. Until I saw its head was gone. How do you kill something without a head? Smash every inch of it flat with a hammer? Chop it into mulch with the mower? Not me. Guilty and confused, I mowed another lap around the yard. The snake continued to writhe like a snapped power line. A creature without a head should not do this. A mammal would never do this. Even a beheaded chicken falls over in less than a minute.

By my third lap, the snake's body had subsided to periodic twitches. It had a rich, scarlet-ribbed belly and was too small to harm more than insects. It had red blood like mine, felt pain as I did. It lacked hands, but it did have eyes, organs and senses. I pitied my fellow creature. Bending to pick up the remains with a stick and deposit them in the bushes, I discovered the snake's decapitated head—a stub an inch long—lying crookedly in the grass a few feet away. I bent nearer. Without a body, blood, or heart, the jaw opened to hiss at me. There was no sound, of course, since the head had been disconnected from its lung. I backed away, and the jaw closed. I leaned nearer. The jaw mimed another hiss and revealed a pink throat. Daylight shone through the hole where it had been severed from its body. Hair rose on my arms. The head didn't seem upset at being dead—it was placid when I moved away.

Oh, I know these were reflex reactions in cells not quite dead. But why *wasn't* it totally dead? I slid the hissing head on a shovel and laid it far from the body. Suppose they joined up again?

Such alienness frightens us. Snakes *are* different. They crawl out of their skins a half-dozen times a year. They smell through forked tongues that plug into scent receptors in their mouths to register aromas. Males have two penis-like organs called hemipenes, both of which may be used during intercourse. Anacondas mate in breeding balls of one female and a dozen males that smear sperm over her. This is not life as we know it, unless we count pornography. Snakes challenge our conception of what life is and how it is experienced.

Snakes also unsettle us because they enter the ordinary world by stealth, seem to materialize from another dimension. You hear grass swish, and a six-foot rat snake parts it. You lift mulch from your flower garden, and a brown snake underneath slithers away so fast you are not quite sure it was there. As you prepare to wade into a pond, you notice beside your bare feet the glossy head of a fat, black water snake. They are life's hidden watchers.

Once as my wife, Carol, poured potting mixture from a previously opened plastic bag into a planter, the soil moved. It was a two-foot milk snake—red, black and ivory banded. The colors flashed as it churned out of the black compost—as if the soil itself generated this shiny, brilliant creature. Carol hyperventilated. "I almost reached my hand into the bag!"

I told her the milk snake could have nipped her but usually strangles prey, and that even if it climbed her arm and twined around

'I began this piece by narrating my encounters with snakes. But it remained flat until I accepted that something deeper was going on. Time for research. Reptile science proved to be as

poetic as myth and symbols; I grudgingly came to realize that snake dream-consciousness painfully exposes humans' failure to evolve beyond our primitive, violent origins. At the same time I felt a comic detachment from the reptile "philosophy," much as we regard our own dream state.... You cannot simply write what you already know. Writing must change your ideas or it is merely report writing.'

~ Garrett Bauman

her neck, I assured her it could not squeeze hard enough to kill her. I slid a finger around her throat to demonstrate and received an entirely justified jab in the ribs as thanks.

Some snakes, of course, are truly dangerous. The water snakes in my pond strike aggressively and create nasty gashes that bleed freely because their saliva contains an anticoagulant. A shaken friend of mine back from a trip to Brazil had watched natives cut open a thirty-foot anaconda and remove a dead boy inside. And venomous snakes kill thousands of people each year world wide—many more than sharks, lions, tigers and bears combined. Yet we should be far more terrified of cigarettes or automobile travel if peril were the real issue. No, snakes grip our imaginations far more deeply than mere safety warrants. Gallup Polls consistently rate fear of snakes the most common fear among Americans while fear of public speaking is second, although your chance of being bitten by any kind of snake is less than one in 70,000, while the danger of being called to speak in front of the local library book club or your daughter's fifth-grade class is virtually a certainty.

About 15 million people worldwide own snakes. There are

hundreds of active websites and chat rooms where people trade stories. They don't talk about safety; mostly, they worry about their snakes' appetites. The highlight for many who keep snakes is feeding live insects, amphibians and mammals to them. A friend of mine who owns a green boa trembles with delighted terror as he prepares to drop a twitching mouse into the cage. He's a gentle, sensitive man, yet his anticipation told me *this* moment was what the snake was for. A snake is for annihilation. As he strokes the mouse's head, I wonder if he identifies with it or the snake.

Venomous snake fights have replaced cockfighting and dog fighting as the *chic* battle-to-the-death sport in most of the world. Exotic kraits and black mambas lay their lives on the line for their mostly male owners, for killing, not winning, seems to be the point of these contests. But it is not just obsessed reptile-lovers who have connections to snakes. Although the average person seldom sees snakes, they are the most common animal in human dreams—surveys done over a half century show that about half of us dream of snakes. They have been said to represent death, temptation, evil, and/or sexuality. Freud believed they were phallic; other analysts say they represent the devouring female orifice or the violent sexuality we simultaneously desire and loathe. In India it is said that a serpent sleeps coiled at the base of our spines; our sexuality "awakens" the snake, which travels to our brain to offer us enlightenment. Serpents in our dreams may also symbolize rebirth (shedding skin has even been likened to Christ's resurrection).

It is no wonder, then, that most religions have significant snake myths and symbols. In ancient Greece and Rome, serpents were considered sharp-eyed dwellers of the underworld who could prophesy and thus were often given honored places in temples. The Chinese dragon—a flying reptile—symbolizes vitality. In Asia snakes in myth often appear as teachers. They teach silence, inner control, watching and how to flow around obstacles instead of confronting them. In Asia speaking snakes advise humans about how to deal with human problems. They know secrets we don't.

Such positive symbolism gradually faded in the West with Christian portrayals of the snake as the calculating destroyer of souls, the flesh Satan found most akin to his spirit. George, England's patron saint, is celebrated for slaying a dragon. St. Patrick is praised for driving the snakes from Ireland, although the only snakes he attacked were symbolic ones—nonbelievers. Both eastern and western mythologies identify snakes with fire, guile, and intelligence, and in both cultures snakes are slaughtered.

I like these ideas, but there is a more interesting—and threatening—explanation for why snakes provoke such strong reactions, first suggested in Carl Sagan's book on the evolution of human intelligence, *The Dragons of Eden*. Sagan based part of his theory on the work of Paul MacLean who proposed that our three-part brain mirrors its evolution over the ages in a "microgenesis." MacLean's work continues today in research by such scientists as Spanish neurologist Ruben Rial. The core brain of all higher animals—the one that developed first in evolution—is the reptile brain or R-complex. The second brain, first discovered by French scientist Paul Broca in 1878, is the limbic lobe, which developed on top of the R-complex as birds and primitive mammals evolved. Humankind's advanced neo cortex—both right and left hemispheres—developed atop these two as evolution continued, but the reptile core is still with us.

Sagan believed most of our disturbing dreams are the safe, partial release—when our higher brain is resting—of a reptilian worldview that we suppress during the day. Our reaction to snakes, then, may be a recognition of the cold, emotionless, brutal core inside ourselves that our higher reason tries to control. We reenact within ourselves the evolutionary struggle between reptile and mammal. The R-complex is ritualized, selfish, paranoid; the limbic introduced feelings and altruism (e.g. feeding your offspring instead of eating them); the neo cortex added logic, language, abstract thinking and creativity. Humanity's divided, conflicted self may have its origins in our divided brains. Our mammalian sensitivity, altruism and creativity daily battle our reptilian violent rages, greed and dark ritualism. The reptile brain has not withered away and cannot be fully exorcized because—like it or not—it still controls basic life support functions—breathing, digestion, sensory input and part of our sexuality. The reptile spirit lives on with these functions. It horrifies us—and it is us.

As a child I remember coming upon a mass of newborn snakes on a lawn. Dozens wriggled in a pile ten feet from me, but in a rush of paranoia I felt *surrounded* by them. The image haunted my dreams for weeks. In those dreams I moved inexorably nearer the snakes—gliding in a kind of hypnotic trance—even though I longed passionately to run away. I felt compelled to touch them or let them crawl on me, and was saved only by waking. In this confrontation with vestiges of the reptile within, I was helpless to refuse—terrified yet passively resigned. Snake dancers—Hopi, Haitian, Serbian, Hindu, Vietnamese—who twirl snakes in a mystical frenzy, embrace this primal side of themselves, find release and acceptance of the repressed reptile. But lest we dismiss these dancers as "primitives" from third-world cultures, in the United States the Cult of the Great Serpent celebrates Snake Day June 7 by writhing naked with snakes. In the southern hemisphere, should you be traveling and wish to participate, the Cult celebrates on Dec. 7. The major difference from primitive snake cults is that the twenty-first century one has a website.

I recently watched a half-dozen reptile programs on television. They're remarkably similar. In a typical show, under the guise of learning something about snake behavior, a half-dozen scientists splash through swamps to catch and tease snakes. Afterward a narrator "interprets" the significance of what they learned for science, but the real meaning of the programs occurs when the men and women communally hold the snake—muscular, sensuous and draped over their skin. The cameras dwell lovingly on these moments. It is the feral, deadly, inner self they embrace, barely controlled by a forefinger and thumb around the snake's head.

On other shows, wacky nature showmen seeking reptile "adventures" repeat the ritual. They creep nearer and nearer a deadly snake so the viewers have the sense I had in my own dream of helpless insanity. "Fool! Fool! Go back!" my mammal brain screams as the camera pulls us inexorably closer. Wild-eyed, the man reaches into a dark hole and drags out a rattler or mamba by the tail. As the snake strikes, the man leaps back so the fangs just miss, then wrestles with the beast and holds it up to be seen. The scientists and the showmen are our surrogates, dragging our deadly, reptilian selves out of the darkness. We are repelled and mesmerized at this reenactment of our inner psychic drama.

How else can we explain brutal orgies of herpetecide, mostly against rattlesnakes and copperheads. With sticks, guns and the occasional flamethrower, the mammals attack snake-dens when they gather to mate or hibernate. They pile up thousands of reptile corpses, make belts and headbands of the skin, and eat the flesh. Does such butchery exterminate the hissing in their human brains—or embrace it? From an emotional standpoint, these massacres differ only marginally from the scientists who hunt and measure snakes, milk their venom and draw their blood. But what of those who scoff at snake myths and dreams as empty superstition, as irrational demonizing of a creature that simply reacts to stimuli in a defined logical way? Are these people dispassionate and clearheaded—or are they kidding themselves?

A few years ago, my wife found a yellow racer in the garden with a toad in its mouth. The snake contracted its muscles to work the toad farther in. Carol sprayed water from the hose at them until the snake lost its grip, and the toad escaped. She celebrated, but despite myself, I pitied the hungry snake. Let's try an imaging game. Imagine yourself as a snake. Embrace the reptile memory slithering through the algae-coated swamps of your brain. Reverse evolution and regress like a video on rewind back through millennia. Your hands and feet atrophy and disappear into your trunk. Scales close over your soft, sensitive skin and translucent scales cover your eyes. Sink to the ground and catch moving food in your mouth.

How else does it feel to be a snake? With no neo cortex, you cannot retain thoughts or images. Snakes are notoriously poor learners, far worse at mazes than mice. For them, each day—each hour, each minute perhaps—is dissociated from the next. It is as if you awaken each moment and all your previous life is a vague, fading dream. This is MacLean and Sagan's best guess at what snake consciousness might be. Snake consciousness when awake eerily resembles our dream state. In fact, Sagan says our R-complex, unleashed at night when the high brain functions go dormant to recharge, creates many of our dreams.

We believe the most far-fetched things in dreams. While the higher brain sleeps, no logic represses the reptilian paranoia that hears gremlins clawing at the gates. Snakes never doubt—the whisper of skepticism comes from our little neo cortex watcher, who sometimes in humans' most terrifying nightmares stirs itself to see what stupidity its irrational cousin is cooking up. The stirring neo cortex is the voice that tells us while still asleep, "Oh, it's only a dream." The vulnerability and paranoid illogic of our dream world suggest how snakes perceive all existence. We "forget" most dreams because, upon reawakening, our neo cortex censors the drivel produced while it was dormant and focuses us on the real world.

Snakes have no limbic system to allow them to feel empathy for others. Curiously, this state occurs in our dreams too. When our limbic brain goes into "quiet mode," we calmly accept the most horrible or fantastic events without them hurting us. Sometimes we are even indifferent to our own fate. "Look how fast that truck is coming toward me. Oh, I'm going to die. Mmm." Because our neo cortex is resting, language ability is depressed in our dreams. Images are vivid, but we cannot name things or people we "know." We feel separated from ourselves as if by a thick gauze wall. And indeed we are. We cannot explain ourselves or even say what our name or address is—because we are the other self then, the one who has not mastered language. In our reptile dream life we live in a world of disconnected moments and images such as the mentally ill often experience—strangely ritualistic and stark, filled with odd fears and aggressions that arise for no particular reason.

When I watched interviews with serial killers and child molesters and when I counseled jailed prisoners, what always struck me was their inability to empathize. In therapy they are repeatedly told what their victims suffered, what the survivors suffer, but they don't understand. They grope through a surreal world in which feeling is inaccessible to them. They know other people feel something that they do not. Even when they say the right words, it's done mechanically—and you know the snake brain has won a victory or the neo cortex has failed. It is no accident, I think, that mental illnesses such as obsessive compulsive disorder, post traumatic stress disorder and panic disorder have been traced to the R-complex part of the brain.

The R-complex, according to MacLean, is dominated by the mechanical, the limbic by the emotional, and the neo cortex by the rational. He suggested that each part has a distinct *personality* with its own sense of space and time, its own style of intelligence, its own "attitude." The significance of this to me is that it challenges our notion of selfness. It explains why we often do not feel like one person. Humans' limbic and neo cortex regions have bonded fairly well, with lots of solid neurological connections between them. We also speak of "right brain" and "left brain" thinking, although these halves of our neo cortex are the best-integrated parts of our brain, and each can perform functions for the other half if it is damaged. But the R-complex, forever repeating its patterns mechanically—heartbeat, breathing, digestion—has been isolated and chained to its monotonous tasks, so the bounding neo cortex could scurry up evolution's ladder and learn wonderful things and play with feelings and creativity. The neo cortex evolved so rapidly, there are only skimpy, tenuous connections between our reptile brain and the higher lobes. The snake is loose inside us—and when the neo cortex rests at night, it crawls into our dreams to have its say. Which of these brains is us? Who of us is *not* schizophrenic?

Snakes scare me in lots of ways.

In human dreams—and perhaps in snakes' waking lives—motives seem alien and emotionless. In dreams, our flesh disobeys us, becoming paralyzed despite our desire to defend ourselves or run. For brief moments we can follow what is happening, then magical events intrude. For the water snakes this happens when I appear at the pond and loom over them as they soak up sun beside their frog paradise. There are two big ones, one black, one brown, I see regularly. I call them Adam and Eve. To them I am the unnamable intruder, the sudden, unexplained shadow that blocks the sun. *I* spook *them.* They slither into the water in a daze, then turn to poke heads above the surface to stare at me. I can almost hear them thinking, what *is* that big thing? Will it eat me, or should I try to eat it? So far, they have decided to swim away into the weeds, but I wonder if some day they will be curious about what new knowledge I might offer them. I am the devil of reason and purpose in their innocent, confused world. I am the thing they might be, could their brains stretch into that other dimension.

Since ancient times, people have noticed the calculating demeanor of serpents. Snakes pay attention. Perhaps they have an urge to figure things out, but lack the mental tools to do it. Yet oddly enough, snakes have one evolutionary advantage over humans. They have an unrestricted ability to grow new brain cells throughout their lives, which suggests a greater potential capacity for learning than humans, who grow new brain cells at a much-restricted rate. Researchers like David Holtzman, formerly at the University of Rochester, has found that young snakes can learn faster than people previously thought, and he teaches them to adapt to stimuli rather than simply react mechanically. He has been especially successful at teaching snakes to escape mazes and traps. Will they be able to pass down this ability to learn at higher levels in ensuing generations? We know reptiles had the capacity for the great leap forward that led to mammals and humans in millennia past. Yet evolution has not gifted them with higher brains. Do they sense their innate, unfulfilled capacity?

This is purely subjective, but I sense a frustrated arrogance in snakes. They think they deserve to be the "lords of life" as D. H. Lawrence once described them. I'm glad they don't have the hands, concentration and memory to make tools. I wish Holtzman would not teach them new tricks. They have enough already. Humans—despite our supposed empathy and altruism—have plenty of uncontrolled, heartless brutality inside us, and I'd be happier if we had a tighter leash on that. Holtzman is scarcely alone. Snake farms and snake sperm banks are rapidly breeding "improved" snakes for commercial purposes—brighter, larger, faster, and more skilled in fighting. Humans are literally boosting snakes up evolution's ladder. Today, researchers are experimenting with gene-splicing—giving snakes chromosome implants from mammals—that might accelerate the process. How about a coral snake with hands? Or a furry, warm-blooded rattlesnake that does not need to hibernate? A cobra that can think?

An Indian myth may be instructive. In it, a ravenous snake demon eats everything in the world as it grows bigger and bigger. When all is devoured, its appetite is still unsatisfied, so it eats the world itself. Then it complains to the god Shiva that there is nothing left to eat. Shiva suggests, "Why not eat yourself?" and the demon does until it disappears into the void of its own maw. We are fascinated by snakes' ability to swallow things larger than themselves—for our species has such *hubris* too. As human technology races ahead of our emotional evolution, we are far more likely than snakes to devour the world and ourselves. Yet the snake is a useful symbol. The snake is an annihilating hole into which things vanish. Its terror is nothingness, and the terror of our three-part brain is akin to it. Each of us is not a singular "I," not even a "we" composed of sibling selves, but simply an illusion, a void that swallows itself. Our personality cannot be pinpointed. If "I" see by night through reptile eyes and by day through mammal eyes, if my brain, like a computer is simply a series of windows now open, now closed, where is this "I?" Can a self be simply the platform on which these images run?

One spring day, I heard rustling in the woods. I waited quietly, and soon prey and predator passed within a foot of me. First came a tan wood frog with its distinctive black facemask. It stretched when it leaped, hands grasping at the air ahead for extra inches. It skidded sideways, gathered its legs and sprang again and again. Behind it came a big garter snake with a yellow stripe. I waved to scare away the snake, but it was so intent on the frog that it ignored me. I followed, so the three of us made an evolutionary procession of sorts.

I watched from high over them with the broad perspective of my evolutionary advantage. When the frog changed directions, the snake paused, raised its head above the grass and rotated it like a periscope, sniffing with a flicking red tongue, its mouth in a stony grin. As it spotted the frog, the garter snake wagged its tail—a slow, satisfied wag that made me shiver. I wanted it to be colder, more mechanical. I wanted no signs that it had even a trace of the higher brains, no hint of emotions. Keep in mind this was a country snake, not educated in university labs or improved with gene splicing. The chase went around trees and bushes, the snake showing a dog-like joy in hunting.

Finally, the wood frog made for a fallen log, squeezed under it, then from the other side leaped on top of the log, and squatted motionlessly behind a knob. It was worthy of a trick from *Last of the Mohicans*. I cheered for it. I hoped the snake would slither under and keep going. When it did disappear underneath, I winked conspiratorially at the frog. I felt happy, even reassured somehow. I scooped up the wood frog and carried it twenty yards away. It lay placid and cool in my palm and—surprisingly—did not urinate on me.

Quickly returning to the log, I saw no sign of the snake. Would it slither away in dejection? I waited. Nothing. I peeked under. It wasn't there. Puzzled, I rolled the log. The snake's tail trailed from a rot hole in the wood. As the log rolled all the way over, the rest of the snake spilled out. Halfway into its mouth was a green frog. The garter snake's jaws were achingly distended like slip-joint pliers compressing the bulging frog, and the reptile thrashed to gain greater purchase on the victim. The frog kicked a few times, but that only helped propel it deeper into the throat. This calmed the snake, content to wait for the frog to kick itself into oblivion. The snake spotted me at last and raised its head high, defiantly grasping the frog like a trophy. "This is mine!" it seemed to say. "I've had enough of your intrusions! Get out of my world!" The snake's eyes seemed to blaze with emotion researchers say it does not have. By now only the frog's legs remained unswallowed, hanging from the corners of the snake's mouth like a giant mustache.

The snake must have picked up the new scent under the log and poked into the green frog's hole with gaping jaws. The frog's secret bunker became the perfect trap. No exit. The snake's maw filled the opening, and I shivered picturing that approaching pink, cottony void stretching from floor to roof to take my own head into itself. The mouth slid closer. For the snake is always waiting for opportunity. I considered rescuing the green frog as my wife had the toad, but this one was down the throat so far that I would have to kill the snake to do it. I had a hatchet in the barn, but did not get it. In a kind of trance—a kind of dream paralysis—I waited in horrible, helpless elation for the frog's feet to disappear.

Britton Gildersleeve
Anomie

'The limits of my language are the limits of my world.'
~ Wittgenstein

*P*laces speak their own languages. Cities, neighborhoods, even the individual rooms of houses each have their own private language. There is a rise and fall like the tonal musics of Vietnamese and Thai—six ways of meaning.

In the rooms I wandered as a child, the bars on the windows whispered to me of Ali Baba's forty thieves, stealing through the dark into the villa. They sang songs of Hanuman, monkey warrior, flying through the night. And other times they were simply bars: In the still heat of the afternoon, when the house was napping, I would slip between them to sit on the tiled roof, trying to translate what it knew.

You can come to identify with the language, the fragrance, the textures of a place so strongly that they become a part of you. The French call it *goût de terroir*, the taste of the landscape: soil and rain and rock inflect taste—the perfume of grapes, the crumb of cheese. We taste this in wine, in tea, in chocolate. Outside of Naples, the San Marzano tomato blends the volcanic minerals of Vesuvius into the tart flesh of the ultimate pizza tomato, and wine labels bear their birth certificates proudly, the seal of aristocratic geography. Each of us becomes what we depend on for sustenance, tied to the places where we grew. Even if we can never call those places home.

My earliest beginnings were in grief, although I was a child of privilege, loved and cared for. The child of two matriarchies, I did not see my father—away at war—until I was almost two years old. In my grandmother's scrapbook of our lives, next to the picture of my father's return from that war—doll clutched in one large hand, daughter in the other—is a yellowed clipping of a very different father: the

'I revised this piece so many times—adding, subtracting, changing ... maybe because like all my work, it bridges the gap between what I experienced and what I know/feel about that experience. To paraphrase Forster, how do I know what I feel until I see what I write? Writing isn't just about the words on the page, but about living and how you construct it... about exploring who you are, what the world expects you to be, mapping an intellectual and emotional cartography. And being able to send those maps out again, rejection after rejection after rejection....'

~ Britton Gildersleeve

man who shot a woman to save his own men, killed a young woman—perhaps a mother—quickly, efficiently.

"He had to, you know," my grandmother would assure me, as she fingered the yellow clipping, dated so close to my birth day. So that from the very beginning, I knew there was war.

My father came back from it.

My husband changed in it.

I grew up shadowed by its ghosts.

Like I grew up with my mother, my grandmothers, my great-aunts and aunts, the company of women marking me in ways I can't always name. In the house my father bought for my grandmother, my mother and me, women cooked and laughed and cried and told stories over tea and coffee and long nights of waiting. In those hot Oklahoma nights, barely cooled by the damp dirt-fragrant mist of the old water cooler, we sat together in the living room.

"Claude never did go out with that woman again," my grandmother would tell, her gray eyes almost blue with laughter.

"I should have known about Earl then," my Aunt Ina would mourn, shaking her head.

And when Uncle Clete died, we folded Aunt Bonnie into us, into our house, absorbed her grief and held her as she cried. "He's too young," she said over and over. "What will I do?"

Carol, my mother's youngest sister who still lived at home, curled my ponytail, made up my face with lipstick and Grandma's powder rouge, and walked me three blocks down Birmingham and one block over to Bob's Grocery, where I would watch Mr. Grady slice slices from a block of frozen chili. He would wrap them in white paper on the glass counter, and hand them over into my keeping. This was a language I learned early: the precision of a sharp knife making dinner, the transfer of food from one hand to another. With food we were safe—it was a kind of love anyone could offer, love no one ever refused.

I learned to cook first from Aunt Bonnie, later from my mother-in-law. Like most of us, I picked up a few things from all over, but in our family "all over" meant from the old ladies.

"The aunts," my husband Glen still calls them, long-dead and their blue and silver hair vivid only in my memories: Grandma, Aunt Bonnie, and Aunt Ina. Sometimes Aunt Velma and Aunt Erma, sometimes Aunt Gussie or Aunt Anna.

But mostly Aunt Bonnie. I never learned anything about cooking from Aunt Ina, just cleaning. She was very clean, even when she began to think that the man down the street was demon-possessed, and that a clean garage was a passport into heaven. I don't remember anything about her cooking. If cooking is really about life and love, like M.F.K. Fisher says, then maybe that's why. Aunt Ina wasn't very happy, even then. But Aunt Bonnie, Grandma, Aunt Velma, Grandmother... all my other old ladies cooked the way they loved me, with generous abandon. I learned the most *real* cooking from Aunt Bonnie. As far back as I can remember, she was cooking. Green beans cooked 'til tender with salt pork and pearly new potatoes; creamed turnips soft and slightly sweet in a blanket of buttery white sauce. Apricot fried pies, the apricots fresh-picked from the backyard apricot tree that was part of my birth, the crust hot and melting around the gooey sweet filling. I would burn my mouth every time because I just couldn't wait to taste.

"Honey, just wait a bit, and it'll be cool," Aunt Bonnie would shush me. But I could never wait, and I would toss the hot half-moon pie from hand to hand, nibbling little bites from the fork-crimped edges.

Aunt Bonnie made cobblers too, rhubarb and peach and sometimes blackberry. The tart fruit feeling sandwiched between the sugar-crackled crust, the layers brightly colored and redolent of butter and sugar and the summer's harvest. When I was nine, and had to have my leg operated on, the doctor asked me to think of my favorite things as I lay waiting for the anesthesia to take effect. I began to list them, mumbling from under the mask: Aunt Bonnie's chicken and rice, and skillet cornbread melting with butter, and sweet Porter peach cobbler to finish it all off. I swear that doctor looked hungry as I lay under the mask looking up at him. And that's what I dreamed of, Aunt Bonnie's Saturday meal.

Chicken and rice wasn't good enough for Sunday dinner. Sunday dinner had to be roast, or pork chops, or fried chicken, which Grandma always made. Aunt Bonnie did the "everyday" cooking, but Grandma made the "special" fried chicken—crust shattering in your mouth into a hundred flakes of brown. Grandma and Aunt Bonnie lived together, had ever since Uncle Clete died when I was four, when Aunt Bonnie came over in tears. She and Grandma, already widowed, clinging to each other while I peeked around the door into the big bedroom. They had a double wedding and now a double widow-hood, they said.

We all thought of it as Grandma's house, but my father bought it. He set it up for Grandma before I was even born. After Uncle Clete died, Aunt Bonnie came to sleep in the front bedroom, the only real bedroom the tiny house had. Grandma slept on the back porch, which Uncle Charlie turned in to a sleeping porch, surrounded on three sides by large windows that opened onto the backyard garden. He replaced the rusty old screens with roller windows, clear glass swinging out into the back garden, the bedroom light changing with the Oklahoma weather.

In the summer, if you lay quiet between the cotton sheets still scratchy from hanging on the clothesline, fragrant with summer sun and the peonies that bloomed where the sheets brushed them as they almost touched the ground, you could hear crickets and the sound of June bugs hitting the screened windows. If you were unlucky enough to sleep during the day—consigned by behavior or illness to an afternoon nap— you lay on the smooth sheets, under the breeze from the big fan at the end of the room. It swept across you, moving the air from the kitchen, with its smells of hot fried chicken and cobbler, to the garden, with its own smells of roses and hot grass and water from the sprinkler falling against the dusty walls of the old shed.

It was a Southern kind of house, deep eaves and tall windows and the screened-in back sleeping porch. On the front porch there was a dusty red glider; you sat on its metal lattice work until there were deep imprints on the back of your sweaty thighs. There was a cooler in the dining room that cooled by spraying a mist of air that came through musty, mildewed vents. Summer in Grandma's and Aunt Bonnie's house meant hard scratchy grass in the back yard, and coming in through the back storm door into the dining room, where you stood in front of the cooler until you traded your hot sweaty red cheeks for the cooler's fine mist.

We were, I realize now, a Southern kind of family, although I didn't think so then. I suppose, when and if I thought of it at all, I saw us as just like everyone else. Children mirror the idiosyncracies of their families, legitimating difference, eccentricity, even craziness, through their acceptance. We were Southern crazy. Not the inbred crazy of my friend Tracy's West Virginia backwoods family, but the nothing-I-do-could-be-wrong crazy of my Grandmother Britton's Kentucky "landed gentry." If her son, my father, thought that we should have a playhouse, then he saw nothing wrong with buying a small open horse-trailer and roofing it with canvas for me to use in the driveway. If my grandmother, a *grande dame* of the first order, thought we should have posture and ballet lessons, then by God we would get them, even when my father was trying to feed three children and a wife on a light colonel's half-pay retirement. That's just what you did.

When I was little, and just starting to learn about the feeding of a large family like ours, I was only allowed to watch the aunts clean up. Once I was one of the "big girls," I could help bring the dishes from the carved dining table to the old-fashioned sink in the kitchen. You could bathe a four-year-old child in that sink, and we sometimes did. It held an enormous roaster with ease—the aftermath of an extended family's holiday feasting—neatly napped with lemony detergent suds. After one aunt had emptied a dish and put the carefully wrapped leftovers into the icebox, another washed the dish clean in the soapy sink, handing it off to a third to dry. There were always plenty of aunts.

I knew I had officially passed from little girl to big girl the day I was offered the copper-bottomed pots to polish. Kitchen jewelry! I took out the white and copper-lidded jar of Twinkle, and carefully restored each scorched and burned surface to pristine gleam. Years later, in a kitchen half a world away—a slum in Algiers—I would stand once again on a stool polishing copper-bottomed pans. Outside the window of that life, instead of Oklahoma rain and sunlight, was the ventilator shaft of a third-floor walk-up, and my neighbor Saliha with ten children chattering to me in French. It felt surprisingly familiar.

There are so many ways of speaking. My grandmother's small

house, for years the only home I believed in, held within its rooms the ghostly sound of apricot blossoms drifting onto pale grass in spring. My grandmother planted that apricot tree the day I was born. The earth shook, the only earthquake recorded in the town where I was born. While my father, halfway around the world, took a nameless young woman's life in payment for men whose names he held like ransom for his unnamed daughter, the earth rumbled thunder and tectonics. Yet another lifetime and half a world away, Saliha, across the ventilator shaft affianced to her husband, she 14, he 30. Each of us connected by the thinnest of threads....

*

Between women there is always the language of biology. The down-drift of blood, the double syllable of heartbeat. A friend once told me that naming this "shared" is essentialist, rejects plurality. *No.* While it is true that the woman who bared her breasts to me in a dark hall in Hussein Dey, Algiers, begging for money to feed her nursling, bleeds to the same moon that I do, this does not make us "sisters." Nor does either of us have a clue what the other is thinking. It means only that when women traveling a hundred different roads gather, our bodies link us in our fragility, our dependency, our resilience. Immeasurably closer than childhood friends is Saliha, the Kabylie woman across the ventilator shaft, joined to me by conversations over polished copper, shared cups of sweet mint tea, lives exchanged like talismans against the dark spaces between men and women.

I can't pretend—I wouldn't want to—that I know what the woman who died that day so many years ago at my father's hands felt. I don't know her age, her name; her face is blank to me. She is only a family story, the mark she left upon a man and the women who knew him. Like a woman I never met in Saudi Arabia, who cooked for me and kept the house where I was a guest. *Yousef's sister.*

Yousef's sister had no name, even when I asked Yousef, whose own name was familiar to me, my husband, our sons. His sister, who fed us lamb and rice and dates, sharp with cinnamon and cumin and oranges.... I will never know her name. But I know that I am no more like her on any fundamental level than I am like the sea that whispers through my blood. And yet sometimes, years after I last ate dates stuffed by her hands, sat at plates polished by her hands, I wonder about her face and name, and listen for her stories.

"I will not sell my sister into marriage," Yousef would tell my husband (never talking directly to me, another woman whose name he did not say aloud). "Not as my mother's father did to her," he would add. Yousef a good man, driven by good intentions—a woman not chattel, he was trying to tell my husband, tongue-tied by culture and language and the narrow corridors of male communication.

So that Yousef's sister was a ghost in her own house, nameless and faceless and outside of a world where the only language that could gain her entrance was the language spoken by a mother, by a wife. The languages of the women of my family, whose eyes opened like windows into rooms I never knew until I married. Their stories changed like my own body after birth, after the week it took us to name our firstborn son. But bodies are not language—they can only frame it, try to translate it, place breath and sound into one package and mail it to another.

*

As an eight-year-old child whose hair hung behind her like the tail of a Palomino pony, I knew that my body was alien to everything around me. Standing in the marketplace of a lost city shaped in equal measure by war and elegance, the reaching hands of dark-haired women told me that my hair was different, my skin different, the shape and taste of unfamiliar language on my tongue... different. Standing in the *grand marché* of Saigon, recognizing the utter singularity of my body, I first began to see how we live at the nexus of place, body, gender. All of these the soil in which language grows.

My mother, still running from the two-dress poverty of her childhood, told me proudly that we were diplomats; my friends called us expat brats. I only knew we didn't fit—Vietnam cut too large and tropical for us, we who looked so much like French colonials, so little like the women I loved and wanted to be. Slender graceful women with black hair like a pour of dark water down willow backs, pedaling bicycles down a tree-lined street, as rare and lovely as orchids. As unlike my aunts as I would be.

I sought some key that would tell me who I was, and where that girl belonged. From the onset of memory, I seemed to recognize that home is tangled with body, with the physical and material, but also with self. With belonging. That blonde child, who stood behind the iron gates of privilege while a girl unbearably close to her own age offered up an infant swollen with hunger, knew early on that love is not enough. All you have to carry with you in our migration from birth to death is your body. Growing up at the mercy of wars, of evacuations, aware even at age eight which of my belongings I could fit within one suitcase, I grew to depend on my body. This I could take with me. This I could, hopefully, get out of a war zone. This is all we really own, all I can offer the gods who are so often beyond logic. We are no more than turtles.

That market, with the lepers standing sentry at the entry, where the lacquer fish swim swim swim on the plaques and albums in the last corridor of the last alley, is still my home. Even now, as my two sons ready for their own families, leave this home we've made so far from there and then, I dream in the polyphonic music of a language never familiar. Although when I sit by the counter of a favorite restaurant, I am once again a child, surrounded by the fragrance of jasmine rice and *nước mắm*... I can almost understand the cook's banter. Something in the rise and fall of her dipthongs, her nuanced *bá, bâ, bà*... This is the language of my childhood, as familiar as the soft Southern vowels of great-aunts and plain aunts and almost aunts and sisters.

*

And even if I wanted to disavow these former lives, I couldn't. We are what we have known, where we have been, what we have spoken, eaten, touched and loved. Our knowledge of each language's syntaxes, structures and contextual meanings becomes increasingly unfamiliar as we venture further into territories of translated meanings and cultures, like a shore at high tide is hidden by incoming waters. The country of translation—like that swallowed shore—is a liminal space between two seemingly familiar places, meeting in strange and disturbing blendings. Words shift in meaning like sand underfoot, and meaning is no more containable than water seeping through cupped hands. To speak another language well is to think in that language, to be shaped and colored by a world-view that provides a skeletal framework for meaning. Ironically, the deeper the understanding of the language and culture, sometimes the more difficult the translation. I can translate the Thai *wai* as a bow with hands pressed flat together, held before the chest. Infinitely more diffi- cult to translate the degrees of social recognition implicit in its nuances: how high the hands, how deep the bow. And yet the body schooled in such actions remembers with a kind of muscle memory the precise intonation of the hands' position.

And what does any of this—a circle that twines around my body, only to end up where it began—have to do with lyric and travel and hunger and home, with words that trace the heart's migrations as often as the body's? Nothing. Everything. Women are, Hélène Cixous tell us, always writing with their bodies. And to do so in a world dominated by logic and power and men and Western dualism is to speak—to write—in translation.

Growing up speaking two languages, I knew that ink was my true language. It seems elementary: writing *is* translation. To interpret one human's longing for another is to translate the language of one body, one being, into a language that unites two separate and disparate experiences. Writing is always to speak for those who do not/cannot speak for themselves, as Adrienne Rich argues eloquently, working against an "apartheid of the imagination."

I translate places: the fragrance of cinnamon that once haunted every Algerian bakery, infusing bread and flour, blending the savory with the sweet; the thin, clear light that is desert twilight on a Saudi *djebel*; the attenuated twilight that stretches impossibly thin in the summer night over Amsterdam. These places color who I am today, frame with exotic details my ordinary life. To try to capture in the net of words how sand becomes your breath during a *shamal*, how you turn your back to it and step slowly backward, leaning into the wind's wall, wrapping your baby tight within the safety of your shirt, like a hundred hundred Saudi women are doing at the same moment... How can words carry meaning outside the boundaries of our separate individual experiences? What woman who has climbed down a slippery metal hand ladder into an Oklahoma storm cellar, to escape a tornado's fury, sees in the yellow ozone sky the violent anger of sand and wind?

How can words lay themselves like a bridge between the unfamiliar and experiences that resonate with recognition? How can a trip to the market in Alger evoke the labyrinth of Bangkok's markets, or the *suks* of Dammam, when the spices differ in fragrance, and the sing-song palaver of merchants curls around three or four or even five languages? But a farmer's market in Oklahoma is still a market, selling fragrant Stillwell strawberries instead of bristling *rambutan*. To make that connection between earth, its worker, the fruit of a real person's hands, and the basket I will eat from later that afternoon, is to stand on a dirt floor of words, in any market around the world: the one in Bangkok, where I buy purple-red *mangosteen*; the one in Dammam, where I juggle pistachios hot off the brazier; the one in Puerto Vallarta, where I take home limes for the evening's salsa. The exchange of worn bills and unfamiliar coins—piastres or dinars or pesos or dollars—is less about money than it is about connection. Unlike a supermarket, with its aisles of generic cereals and cookies, a market's brands are the tomatoes of the man from down Route 66 who raises heirlooms, and cajoles me into tasting one, to "get beyond its butt-ugliness." A market is not about convenience: human connection is too messy to be convenient. And the translation implicit in the words we choose to paint the fragrance of peaches and the odor of meat, death in the naked rabbit hanging from its crossed and tied feet, and birth in the double-yoked eggs still lightly smeared with mother's blood, the delicate chartreuse leaf and vivid scarlet fruit... No one needs a dictionary for these. In the specificity of words that we do not recognize is the common weekly journey of women across the world: buying food, making meals, creating home from shelter.

It is the way my mother held me, fed me, wiped my face as I sobbed from Tulsa to San Francisco, a long flight away from my grandmother, who would surely die in my absence. *I close my eyes and all the world falls dead...* Away from home. With boxes of Kraft dinner and tins of applesauce my mother tried to recreate familiarity, the job of mothers long before boxes and cans. In our rooms she hung curtains and tailored bedspreads, wrapping us in pink-and-white safety. It is how, on hot days out of school, she would take me with her to the *Cercle Sportif*, where I would lay on the sticky blue mats spread over the Sports Club's polished wood floor, and lift my legs, half the length of hers, into the air. Bicycling, bicycling. Where were we trying to go?

*

In Islam, the journey to Makkah is called *hadj*—it is the journey every true believer must make at least once in a lifetime, wrapping the body in white and traveling west or east, as if movement might propel one into faith. But while the pilgrim on *hadj* always heads towards Makkah, to end her journey kneeling in front of the black stone of the Ka'aba, merit still accrues to the *hadji* who sets out on the journey, even though she does not make it all the way home. In the history of Islam, many pilgrims die on the road, never attaining the Arabian Peninsula. What they leave to mark their passages are words, maps for other pilgrims who follow.

Saudi Arabia in the late 1980s was as much an intellectual desert as it was a lunar landscape of craters and silt. A woman could wander her own *Rhub al'Khali*—her own Empty Quarter—for years, lost. If you count the millions that the Saudis spent on greenification, your private deserts were more barren. In the eight years I lived there, the Saudis made their deserts bloom, at least in the places where they had planted windbreaks, watered them from tanker trunks, nurtured and tended acacia, bottle brush and cacti, so that satellite photos taken 10 years apart show different horticultural topography. No one mapped or tended our withered dreams, our desperate isolations.

In the smallest of towns—the company compound—I traded my mother's china for acceptance. Like Isak Dinesen, I unpacked the trappings of privilege, and for my sons' sakes, worked to fit in. This I learned from my own mother—I should have been better at it. But it led me to the edge of silent, noteless suicide. I reached out for words, starving for someone who could put a name to the *anomie* I carried within. Someone who could translate my single terror into community.

Cixous, familiar with being the woman, the foreigner, with living in the labyrinthine cities of North Africa, drew for me a map that made sense of what I had been trying to locate in that wasteland. She recognized the danger attendant upon writing as a woman, that language is inadequate, and yet it's all we have. And she tied that knowledge of inadequacy back to the word's divorce from the body, the fissuring of experience into what we can communicate through language, and that which eludes our linguistic attempts. "The Voice," she told me, "sings from a time before law, before the Symbolic took one's breath away..." Taking one's breath away: the breath that shapes the image into words... experience and myth and icon carried on our living breath. I listened, and after years of silence, I began to write. Within three months I was on a plane home, suicide receding like the white nightmare of the desert.

*

In Vietnam and Thailand I learned to believe that time is not only *not* linear, it is not even circular. Instead, think of time as spherical, moving out from a center point that is the consciousness of the thinker, although all of us are webbed together. But if you view time in that manner, what you see is time coextant: you can reach out to change yesterday as easily as tomorrow. And perhaps the woman I once was knows now that she will find friends. Will find words. The words of no place, Bella Brodzki argues: "to speak and write from the space marked self-referential is to inhabit... no place." This is where I found language, in *anomie*. In the place that has no name, no passport, no laws. A place without customs of the country. Like so many other displaced persons, I am always trying to write myself home. Even inner life is a migration: the following of the breath.

*

Buddhism—particularly Zen—says that in the essentials, in the stripped-down bones of the real and the abstract, we find meaning. A Tibetan Buddhist skull cup—once made from the skull of a dead monk—is not simply a reminder that life is transient, but is also a material memory of the dead. The cup is functional, a quality as important in the real as memory is in the abstract, and the cup melds these elements in the bones of being. So the brushstroke of the incomplete circle that stands for enlightenment not only signifies a real state for the Buddhist, but art for the sake of beauty.

With this frame in place, breath becomes the icon of the contemplative space Zen offers in counterpoint to every day's experience. Paradoxically, it also marks life's irreducible necessity: air in, air out. It is in this paradox, in Zen's slippery language of illogic and intuitive leap, that poetry thrives. Trinh Minh-ha once said that the language of Zen was never meant to lead to vicarious "knowledge," but rather to experiential "wisdom." Its intent is to replicate—as far as possible—the experience of the writer/speaker/knower. To make accessible that crescent that lies outside the group's language and experience. To translate, into language, experience. Since I was a small child trying to paint with inadequate words the vivid colors and fragrances of the places that passed for home, I swam in translation. Biting into vowels and consonants, tasting dipthongs on my tongue, trying to find a way to translate difference—my own and that of the places I called home.

I try to draw the high iron gates of the villa on Phan Đình Phùng. I invoke the names of women who combed my hair, women who fed me, sheltered and protected me with their own bodies, curled themselves around my grief and laid their laughter down to make for me safe passage. Brought me pumpkin bread when food was poison. Made me tea when ritual was all that held me tethered to my life. Remembering, I fall into safety.

*

Tess Gallagher said when she was asked to write about the influences on her as a writer that she knew "I would want to get back to the child in me." The child in me lives so far away, in a world so different than the one she grew up to inhabit, that it is difficult for the two of us to talk. But for women, Gallagher reminds us, words are "slow in coming" anyway. They are filtered through the language(s) of our bodies, our bodies that end up abandoned... aging... alone. The downside of growing up in war zones is that so few of us survive. When many of the aging hippies of my generation protested against the Gulf wars, the "faceless Muslim masses" for me had—still have—faces: my neighbor Saliha, affianced at 14, married at 15, mother to 10 living children. Our house help Chandra, plant supervisor with a master's degree who took a job abroad as a house "boy" to support his family, to make a "living" wage. The women who surrounded me in markets in Alger, in Cairo, in Dammam, protected me from street boys w/ their own small white-shrouded bodies, placing themselves around me like a wall. Saudi Arabia is the vegetable vendor in Dhahran, the brass merchant in Khobar. All wars erase faces etched in someone's memory. All wars orphan us from memory.

*

Buddhists find the entire concept of self a kind of fiction, anyway. By ten, I was familiar with *maya*—illusion. I remember wondering if I would disappear overnight, just a dream in someone's fitful sleep. At 12 the Zen *koan* "Am I a man (never a woman, not even then and there) dreaming I am a butterfly or a butterfly dreaming he is a man?" already troubled me: I was never certain. Mostly I remember wondering who I was, what it meant to question my own existence, my sense of exile. This was not something we discussed in my family. Not with my parents, nor my beloved blue-haired ladies: my great-aunts, my grandmothers, my not-quite-godmothers. Each of them seemed firmly attached to the ground on which they walked, rooted in the soil they tended in the garden behind the tiny green-roofed house on Birmingham. I floated above them, like a kite held only by a thin, frayed ribbon. I remember trying to translate my recognition of this sense of non-being into words. Even for nascent Buddhists, the self is a permeable membrane. I knew early on that who I am is inextricably woven into the fabric of the women who raised me, the father who left me, the children who would come after. Even the slippery jewel-toned lizards that crept through the cool tile bathrooms of my childhood were part of me, helping shape and define in some indefinable manner the sound of my name.

Always, the webbedness of the world, the voices of all of us, a kind of Southeast Asian rhythm, the lilting cadence of the Thai culture—supposedly alien, made different by my blonde Midwestern birth—that I have begun, finally, two lifetimes later, to internalize. It is the rhythm of a Buddhist world view—the morning passage of monks, whose mendicant journeys tie dharma to karma for all of us; the drowsy heat of afternoon naps, flies gently waved away from sweaty sleep, never swatted into death; the evening sunset reflected off of the gold spire-like *chedi* of a nearby temple—the easy contemplative nature of life in Thailand that stayed with me, dormant, for the 30 years it has taken me to write my way home.

In Buddhism what you believe influences your practice, a lovely word for what it is that offers meaning to the spaces of our days. A word that tells me I don't have to "get it right," that maybe even the universe doesn't worry about whether I'm "right." That "getting it wrong" is often what words do best anyway, allowing us quite literally to change our minds. Maybe being right isn't even what it's all about. What you practice is your path through this world into the next: it is your path to awakening, to rousing from the deep sleep that passes for attention, and seeing what connects each of us one to another. What we have is the air we breathe in, the air we breathe out. The air held within the chests of each breathing life, as far back as breath crawled from water, walked on land. The air inhaled by each pair of lungs and gills and each cellular organism since time began remains, inflected by the breather, the swimmer, the blindly swimming uninucleate cell... Within the alveoli is the breath of prehistoric fern, the fragrance of cultivated rose, the essence of warrior and mother and hero and child. This is the air that shapes the spaces between the words I practice daily, sometimes for hours, hoping they have the power to save me. Words are my breadcrumb path home. Each phoneme is a marker on the way to who I am, where I belong.

Home. In the breath: the breath that governs the line break is the breath of the symbolic. This is the breath that when followed will lead us home. It is for words to translate our extraordinary ordinary lives—however ephemeral, however like the skull cup—into a form that honors both their terrible beauty and their brutal integrity. It is for words to map this pilgrimage through the imaginary, to provide safe passage for all of us through the shadows of each other's chambered hearts and fragile, temporal bones. Home, to the breath that connects each of us one to another, breath inhaled and exhaled by fire and ash and water and fern and the first blind crawler from the sea. Home to the hearth-stone of memory and desire.

Ralph Ryan
Wildfire Hellfire

*I*t was late November in Southern California, prime time for the Santa Ana winds. Those of us in the wild land firefighting business called them the "Devil Winds."

We'd been called to a fire on the Mt. Baldy Ranger District, on the Los Angeles side of the San Gabriel Mountains. On this night our ten-man initial attack Forest Service helicopter crew was forced to travel by ground carrier. The "Devil Winds" were blowing at 60 mph plus, creating Red Flag Warnings and closing the National Forest to public use. Nonetheless, we were psyched up in anticipation, boasting an attitude of "No Fear." Wild land firefighters are a unique breed and our crew prided itself with the "Can Do" attitude. We weren't cocky, we were confident and loved to fight fire.

As we turned onto Mt. Baldy Road, we got a close up view of our enemy. Flames whipped wildly into the night sky showering red embers down like rain along the wind's path. The red glow dwarfed the darkness, illuminating everything below it. Harold, our foreman, told us to tool up and wait while he and John, our assistant foreman, checked in with the Incident Commander. We rushed out of the carrier grabbing our tools. Adrenaline coursed through my veins. My muscles tightened with strength and my mind reached a state of full awareness. I was ready and eager for combat.

The Ojai Hotshot crew from the Los Padres National Forest joined us. Harold came back and pointed to where the fire was cresting the ridge and ordered, "Listen up; we need to stop the fire from burning down that ridge into the village. Our crew and the Hotshots are the only hand crews available, so we're going to get up there and cut some hot line. Two volunteer fire engines will patrol this road in

'Wildfire Hellfire was one of many hair-raising experiences I lived during a fourteen year wild land firefighting career. It was the most exciting time of my life and after reliving the adventures over and over again in my mind, I've come to the point where I want to tell my story. Transforming thoughts to paper has been as challenging an adventure as it has been enjoyable. I love the craft and strive to put the readers with me, as totally into the moment as possible, to let them feel the intensity. For me, that's the magic of words.'

~ Ralph Ryan

case any spot fires start below us. Any questions?"

The roar of the fire answered.

"OK," Harold shouted, "Lets go."

We began cutting a six-foot wide fire line. My chain saw screamed into the night. Sweat poured off me as I unrelentingly laid chain to brush and oak just before they exploded into flames. I was overcome with a sense of empowerment from stealing the life from the fire as its heat burned on my face. My addiction to fighting wild fires was driven by this intensity and it kept me coming back year after year.

Each time I refueled, I'd look down the line and see the progress. It appeared as though a mini-freeway was under construction; every piece of brush was gone. A cloud of dust hovered over the crew as they scratched down to bare earth with their hand tools. A procession of headlamps swayed in all directions. Half a mile down the slope the lights of the engines patrolling the road were visible.

Our goal of cutting the fire off before it reached the village seemed attainable, but suddenly the weather changed. A strong up-slope wind developed and it eddied onto itself at the ridge top raining hot embers back down the mountain. The gears of our line-building machine came to a grinding halt. No voices were yelling back and forth. Tools went silent.

A frightening roar filled the air and thirty sets of eyes watched in horror as a trail of glowing embers traveled over our heads and settled in the unburned brush below us. I saw little flickers of flames coming to life and strained to hear the sound of water pumps from the engines below. Harold yelled into his radio, "Crew 7-Charlie to the Engine Company on Mt. Baldy Road, come in." There was no reply. He tried again, "Crew 7-Charlie to the engines on Mt. Baldy Road, *do you copy?*" The radio remained silent. Harold was furious and screamed, "ANSWER YOUR GODDAMNED RADIO!" He paced tensely past me a few times with a haunting look. His facial muscles were drawn tight and the veins on his forehead were bulging. He looked like a trapped animal. "What the hell are they doing down there?" he said to no one in particular. I didn't say a word; my eyes were glued on the spot-fires below.

Pushed by the strong up-slope wind, the small fires erupted into a solid wall of flames. They danced wildly over one hundred feet above the brush. I stared in disbelief as contorted fingers of flames completely separated from the fire and whipped above the brush. I pulled out my instamatic camera and took a few shots before the reality of our situation slapped me hard.

We were trapped with no escape route.

I'm thinking we're all going to burn to death until Harold screamed, "Get into the burn and get them off your backs."

The order moved down the line. I watched in a hypnotized state as bodies disappeared into the burned area. He was ordering us to deploy our fire shelters, those little aluminized tents designed to offer some protection against radiant heat, and intended for life-threatening situations only. Deployments were so rare I used mine as something of an expensive pillow. Now it was every man for himself. Superheated air began to burn my nose and throat, and the roar of the fire was so loud I couldn't think straight. I stumbled past John, realizing it's now or never to get my shelter out. I kicked aside as much of the hot embers as I could before ripping the tab off my fire shelter cover. In a matter of seconds, it was open and flapping wildly in the wind. Glancing over to John, I could see he was having trouble with his tab; it had broken off, making access difficult. He yelled, "Does anybody have a knife?" Looking around and then back down at the flames he realized nobody was paying attention to him and frantically began shredding the plastic with his fingers. I struggled against the wind to get my boots around the anchor straps at the bottom corners as my hands slipped into the upper corners. I fell to my knees, pausing a second to confirm that John had his opened, before falling to the ground.

I managed to anchor one corner of my shelter with my web-gear allowing one hand to be free. The fire was sucking the oxygen out of my tent and pulling at my lungs. With my free hand, I dug a small hole in the ground and placed my bandana in it. Frantically, I poured water on it and buried my face in it. Cooler air filled my lungs. Riding on the searing wind, I heard a voice fading in and out. It was Keith's and he was singing....

Oh, the weather outside is frightful
But the fire is so delightful
And as long as you love me so
Let it snow, let it snow, let it snow...

As I'm thinking the poor guy has just lost his mind, a distinct smell began to fill my shelter; I recognized it as Nomex, the chemical used to treat our fire clothes. The radiant heat was baking the chemical right out of my clothing. This catapulted me into sensory overload. My mind was reeling. Why? Why is this happening? What did I do to deserve this? Yet the rapid acceleration into the unknown continued. I raised my head to the sound of rain pelting my shelter. Curiously, I looked up to see orange and yellow light flicker through every crease and seam of my shelter and I realized it wasn't rain; it was red-hot firebrands raining down on me. The head of the fire announced its arrival at my feet with a rumbling vibration so intense it felt as if a freight train were passing over me. The sound was deafening. It intensified to the point where I thought I was going to be crushed to death. Lying in blind submission was more than I could bear; I went into a fit of panic. I wanted to get up and run, but I was only able to push out a defiant, lung-draining scream expecting it to be my last expression in life.

My body began pulsating. I felt like a naked heart pounding on the dirt. I struggled to control my heartbeat, fearing I was going to explode from the inside out. Visions of my parents and siblings flashed before me. My girlfriend beckoned me to her side with her beautiful smile. I repeated over and over again, *please God don't let me die like this, I promise to be a better son, a better brother; a better boyfriend. Just don't let me burn to death... please!*

My fear intensified, time seemed distorted, for all I know it had stopped. Reality came as fragments of my past and I felt myself slipping deeper into despair. A familiar sound pulled me out of my personal hell. It was Harold screaming, "Is everyone alright?"

Life as I wanted it to be returned with every reply. I realized the worst was over. Sheepishly, I raised a corner of my shelter only to see smoke and low flying embers shooting by. I pulled the shelter back down to regain a sense of security. I was safe and wasn't ready to face the outside world. I wanted to stay in this womb-like cocoon forever.

Harold's voice rang out again. This time it was closer and he was swearing, "Those worthless sons-of-bitches." More reason, I thought, to stay right where I was. He was seething with anger and yelled, "Get out of your shelters and line out."

I stood up slowly, keeping the shelter wrapped around me to shield myself from the blowing smoke and embers. I was thinking we should've stayed under longer, but Harold was being driven by his rage. John and Keith emerged with hollow eyes looking as though they had lost the power of thought. Like zombies, we formed a single line and followed Harold out. The once impassable brush field below us was reduced to smoldering stumps.

Ash rose from our pounding feet, choking my lungs and stinging my eyes. We stumbled down the fire line to solid pavement. Our once enthusiastic "Can Do" attitude was crushed. We walked in silence down a road cluttered with ambulances and fire trucks. We were given a wide berth by the crowd that had gathered. By the sheer number of ambulances, I was thinking the Incident Commander had written us off as a body recovery mission. Harold marched us to the first aid station where he immediately went to the command post to get answers to the questions all of us were asking. Where were the engine crews responsible for anchoring the road? And where the hell are they now?

Harold's voice boomed through the staging area. I couldn't make out his words, but he was livid. A few minutes later he returned and said, "The bastards fell asleep. They've been pulled off the fire. A bus is coming to take us to the main fire camp in Glendora."

News of our ordeal had spread quickly through the camp. The servers in the chow line couldn't look me in the eyes as I shuffled past. I was beginning to think we had done something wrong until I was cleaning up at a wash station. The little mirror above the basin revealed a strained face cloaked in black ash. The whites of my eyes were hellfire red leading into a piercing blue. My own face frightened me.

The Village Fire burned over 100,000 acres. It had beaten us into the ground, but only temporarily did it take away our fighting spirit. The main lesson I learned was how quickly the attitude of "No Fear" can be transformed into an intense, life changing realization that to "Know Fear" is far more empowering.

Mil Norman-Risch
The Day My Son Died

*T*he cough syrup was in a bottle on a shelf in the kitchen. He would need something to make him feel better if we were to bundle him up and take him out in this weather.

I wrapped my sweater around me and walked downstairs to the kitchen, where the dishes reprimanded me in the silence of the counter's blue gray light. I opened the cupboard, found the bottle, read the label: last year's Triaminic, a prescription cough suppressant and antihistamine for children under two. It had expired a week ago. Still, it shouldn't matter, and what else could I do? Not only was it the day after Christmas, but it was Sunday, and the doctor's office was an hour's drive to town.

If going for this walk was something we must manage, *as a family*, this was something I could do now. Measure out the half-teaspoon in its plastic dropper.

None of that was difficult. Nor was insisting his sister wear the scarf and mittens, packing up the diaper bag with the bottle of carrot juice, Melanie's sippy cup and cheerios, the Pampers and the extra change of clothes and shoes, just in case, and remembering to grab the cassette tape of Raffi sing-alongs for the car.

After I wiped his nose once more, I zipped him into his hooded coat of gray and white fabric patterned with clouds. *Blond Boy with Curls in Hooded Coat.* Or *Portrait of Zippered Cherub, Framed By Clouds.* I forgave myself for these titles, my need to name things in order to see. He wouldn't mind, if he grew up to learn that his mother had put him to bed saying to herself, "look at this angel face and these golden perfect curls," a sentence that really meant, "Thank you for being a baby who goes to sleep at night. I'm just so tired of everything." He won't mind, I told myself, to learn some day that although I was not grateful for the surprise of the pregnancy so soon after the first, I was indeed grateful for the surprise of his spirit, the easy sleeping blond-curl baby that he was.

The walk was not my idea, I was married to a German. Germans own sturdy boots or walking shoes they spray with water repellent. They walk for hours in drizzling rain, through mud bogs, I learned firsthand when we lived in Sehestedt and then here in Virginia. They traipse across miles of gray-brown barren stubble fields in dim winter light, tossing jokes to each other, gaining tempo, inspired by the fog, the damp, and the destination, nowhere.

The people we were meeting two miles away, at a spot where a new road had been carved into the Goochland County woods to create a rural subdivision that ended with cul de sacs, were Germans.

*

I don't know exactly what I was doing when it happened. We had left our cars at the main two-lane, yellow-striped road, at the appointed meeting spot. We had walked far enough down this rude-sliced road, now new with gravel and exposed to light, that we had settled into separate conversational groupings. Far ahead of me down the road, walking with Mark and his children, was Volkmar, with Melanie riding on his shoulders. Against the gray backdrop of empty winter branches I see their tiny distant figures in my mind now as blots of color—the green of his pants, and above that, the red of his jacket, the yellow of Melanie's coat, the purple dot of her hat. Father and daughter, colors in a vastness.

Susanne, the German woman, was with me, close enough for us to drift in and out of conversation. I was pacing myself with Christopher, holding his hand. *Christopher, a bulge in his cloud coat, the corduroy sausage legs tipping along in his rubber-edged shoes.* These words and images come to me whenever I tell the story, but I didn't think that sentence at the time. I just remember walking and then losing the rhythm. But this happens all the time. Toddlers stumble. And then they walk.

But he didn't.

I pulled on his hand, and nothing happened.

When one tries to retrieve—in all its exactness—a startling moment of awareness, part of the story is really the point before the awareness, the unremarkable vagueness. But what was that? I will say I was looking at bare tree branches without seeing them, I was walking along a gravel road without feeling the gravel, I had Volkmar in my sight but I was not looking at how his figure moved against distant shadows. I was two feet away from Susanne but I was not seeing her hands in her pockets. I will say I was thinking. I was thinking the usual whys, hows, and ifs.

And at that instant when I looked down to find what broke the rhythm of our walk, I was thinking rather than looking.

But there he was, and I saw him: he lay on the gravel, limp, his mouth open, and his eyes rolled back to the whites of his eyes. He looked (but I did not think the word) dead.

The ensuing moments swirl by in memory as images of my impotence: Do I bend down to examine him? Do I take him in my arms? Perhaps, but what I see in memory is my standing there, refusing to move forward in the ghastliness of time, while Susanne kneels down over his body, lifting, fingering, thumping, listening.

'William Blake says it best:
To see a world in a grain of sand
And a heaven in a wild flower
Hold infinity in the palm of your hand
And eternity in an hour.'

~ **Mil Norman-Risch**

Is he breathing? I ask her. She is holding him in her arms. Is he breathing? She looks up, but she does not answer.

And so I know.

I need Volkmar. He needs to know. I see his figure down at a curve in the road in that ghostly forest of bare branched trees, and I startle myself with the volume I summon to yell. Come here. Volkmar, come here! The figure turns. Melanie is on his shoulders. They are far away. Come here NOW. The wave of shame and resignation I feel at that moment is familiar. He might not come. I sense his instinctive reluctance.

But he comes.

They are with the body, turning him upside down like a chicken, holding him by the feet, thumping and clapping. Then I am running. Running up the steep grade of the hill, running for the clearing and the yellow stripe of road. *The mother runs to save her son. The mother's adrenalin accounts for miraculous rescue.* Or *The mother cannot make it to the road in time and so this is the day her son dies.* How long can a brain be deprived of oxygen? How long before saving him means saving him only from death but not from those other bad things? *The day my son began life in a vegetative state.* Even though I am a runner, my stride feels weak, hesitant. I imagine myself stopping to get my breath. *You would do that,* I say, still running. I see Dustin Hoffman, his hair flying backwards as he jerks his head to look behind him, running through alleyways and parking lots, over roadways and bridges, the very image of the power of desire. *You would actually stop. In the movies the person running for his life does not lose faith or speed.*

Everything is blurred and gray. They are far behind me, running now too. I am running for the car, running for Christopher, running for mercy, all of which I know are lost, and at the same time I am running only for the road itself, where in the movie version, someone will be there to save us. But there is only us.

When I reach the main road where our cars are parked, I am not even aware of breathing. I flag down the one approaching car and say it, conscious of the words themselves as words:

"Excuse me, can you help us, I think my son is…. (do I say *dead*?) … is dying." No cell phone. Not from here. Sorry. And they drive away, astonishingly.

Surely too much time has passed now. It's too late now. I know this. But we get into our car, leaving Melanie behind with the others to care for her, and I try not to look at the figure in my lap, this weight in my arms. He is still a little body in a coat. Dense. His lips are the color of his face. His eyes are rolled back in his head. The white between those open eyelids, between those eyelashes, is too terrible. I do not check for breathing. Volkmar is speeding, slinging us hard from curve to curve. At a one-lane bridge over a creek I say, softly, *Great. Now we can all die together. As a family.* I remind myself that couples supposedly pull together in a crisis. The Husband and Wife. Father and Mother with Child. And then we argue. No, not the Goochland Clinic, drive to the gas station! It's not like in Germany! But he bangs over the curb into the parking lot of the health clinic, and we don't even get out of the car to check the entrance doors and signs. The parking lot is one flat stretch of asphalt emptiness. He jerks the car into a backward spin and the gray tracings of tree branches blur cloudy as we pick up speed on the way to the gas station.

Christopher is still a weight on my lap. And now, a minute more is lost, I think. I try not to blame Volkmar, to measure his faults, but I do. Even now. Especially now. And I feel the strange liminality of the moment. Here we are in the space between two things. This is the day my son dies, but because no one has told me yet in words, this is still the part before I know for sure he's dead. This is the waiting part, the gray blue formless foggy part, the part without titles, just the movements and static before the final crystallization. No one can *do* anything.

The car feels like an absurd space for a final awareness, the dashboard as the curved horizon. I tell myself to try something now, here in the car. *Try to save him now*, I say to myself, shamed. I am his mother, after all, and here I am not touching him, not stroking his golden hair, whispering over his body, singing over him, wailing over him. Clouds frame the dead face of my golden boy. I am his mother and I am lost.

What strikes me now as I tell this story, is that my thoughts were these: I did not seek the cause. I did not, strangely, check off names of possible illnesses and syndromes—epilepsy, meningitis, rheumatic fever—nor did I rewind my memory to look for missed signals of his impending collapse. I did not say *maybe it's the cough medicine that expired; maybe the acid changed and it poisoned him.* Or even plainer: I did not say *if only we hadn't come out for this walk in the cold.* With my son on my lap, my son in a cloud coat, I just said, (because I am a person who will not suffer fools or easy fictions,) *this is the day, this is the day, this is the day my son dies.*

There at the grease-smeared desk of the Exxon Station on Route 6 where I dialed 9-1-1, I was conscious again of our total isolation and the absurdity of those moments of drama as they must happen in actual human lives: mine. Here I am, one of those people who call 9-1-1.

I saw the television show in my mind: how every Tuesday night for years Volkmar and I sat in the living room, dinner plates on our laps, listening as the show played tapes of actual emergency calls, and actors then dramatized the story of what was once someone's real happening moment. Surely for us the ambulance will not come as fast. And besides, it's too late. But the people in the show, they believed. A little girl got behind a driver's seat and saved a school bus full of children when the driver fainted. An old man lifted a mangled Mercedez off his wife. Some woman whose brother was trapped in an almost airless cave kept him awake and alive by making him sing along with her for seven hours straight.

The rescue squad arrived just minutes later in answer to my call. They want you to ride in the ambulance, someone said. I got in the back, and sat on a fold-down seat beside the stretcher, where they had tightened wide black straps over Christopher in his unzipped coat. Volkmar rode next to the driver.

The rescue squad volunteer was a tall skinny red-haired boy no older than the students I teach, but because he wore a white jacket, and because he had strapped in my boy, and because he was crouched there with me in the ambulance, looking at red lights on a monitor, and in spite of the words in my head saying, *He's only a boy doing rescue squad work,* I asked him, "Can you just tell me, is he alive?"

"We'll get you to the hospital, ma'am, and they'll be able to help you out." A euphemism, I decided. He knows.

I cannot see much of myself in the scene. But I know I got up, finally, from my seat, to look at my baby, to act like a mother in the movies, a mother who saves children. Or a mother who is able to look at death. You are my little Buddy Man, You are My Boo, You are the

Baby One, You are so good. I sang it as a whisper. His eyelids were closed now.

When you live with lost faith, when you shrug off stories with happy endings, when you know too much or see too much, or think too much, or wish too much, is it difficult to sing? But I made myself sing.

*

And now I come to the end of the story.

We were standing in the hospital emergency room. Christopher lay on the table. His eyes were open. His eyes were blue.

So it was nothing. It had been nothing at all. My son who had died was alive again, a boy with blond hair and blue blinking eyes and with arms that reached and a voice that said "Mommy" and a chin smeared with streaks from a runny nose.

A febrile seizure, caused by sudden spikes in the body temperature of infants and young children, is a rare non-life-threatening occurrence that can have all the signs of death. Sometimes, the doctor was saying, without equipment, even a physician cannot determine whether the child is breathing. That's it.

We had to call our friends to pick us up at the hospital and drive us the thirty-two miles back to that road where we had left our car. In the backseat of one car, and then of the other, on my lap, in the dark, Christopher slept the whole way home.

I have told this story many times. Christopher knows it well. Just two years ago, for her eighth grade English assignment, in the spring when Volkmar found out he had stage four gastric cancer, Melanie wrote a poem titled "The Day My Brother Died." In her poem's version of the story, the brother dies. I guess she felt the poem, being a poem, must end without the miracle.

In my English classroom, most every year, I tell stories, always with the titles first: "The Day We Lost the Gerbils," "The Day I Ran Over My Dog."

"I'm going to tell the story called 'The Day My Son Died,'" I say, knowing they will listen in unbreathing dread. And when I get ready to tell the ending, I wince. I've misled them. It isn't a proper ending. But still there is always a boy in the back of the room, maybe a skinny boy with long legs, or a red-haired boy wearing a zip-up ski jacket, or, this year, a boy named Ben, blond, blue-eyed, with a round face, who wrestles on a team with my own fourteen-year-old son, who wipes his face with the back of his hand, not sorry I see him: full knowing the truth of the title, not sorry for its fiction.

Photo by Jill Krementz

Mother Night ~ Kurt Vonnegut On the Banks of the Big Tennessee

By Don Williams

Hi ho.

Unless the universe has begun running backwards like a run amok player piano, Kurt Vonnegut is dead and not likely to rise again any time soon. But time being what time is, and Vonnegut being who Vonnegut... is... yes, it could happen. Especially if he's like his characters, who bounce around time like pogo riders on checkered kitchen floors stretching to infinity.

Maybe his checking out on April 11, 2007, at age 84, is a way of celebrating lucky deliverance from times too much like those in a favored book—*1984*, by George Orwell—or from a body too bothered by medicinal hocus pocus. Either way, if Vonnegut and Faulkner are right to say the past is with us always, then Vonnegut lives.

See the unkempt hair, moustache and wry grin, lending a huggable quality to the rationalist-humanist even as he ponders frigid truths with every bounce of time's whimsical ride.

A version of this article first appeared in Knoxville Voice, April, 2007.

See the young reporter turned ad man stringing words to push product down the pipeline while honing novels in the 1950s. Watch him quarrel with book marketers who classify *Sirens of Titan* as sci-fi, limiting his exposure to a broader audience, if only for awhile.

Hear the clatter of typewriter keys as he turns notions into print—like the concept of Ice-Nine, an element of Vonnegut's imagination. Careful. One vial of that doomsday weapon would crystallize all the waters of the planet if emptied into, say, the Tennessee River. Something like that happens in *Cat's Cradle*—a title derived from an old parlor game performed with simple string—leaving his frozen protagonist at the end of that novel eternally giving the finger to an eternally frozen universe.

Hi ho.

Maybe young Vonnegut dreams up such images in 1942 as he oh so briefly walks the banks of the Big Tennessee. Inklings of waterways' unity flow into one another, as gathering awareness of Oak Ridge's true purpose flows into darkening visions. Maybe rabid sports worship here on these same banks turn the University of Tennessee mechanical engineering student against such tribal loyalty for all time.

His most controversial novel, *Slaughterhouse Five*, is about a man who goes space-and-time hopping through a universe as shattered as Dresden, Germany in World War II. In 1945, Vonnegut is a prisoner of war there, working in a factory making vitamins for pregnant women, when Brits carpet-bomb the city, a renowned center of culture. Maybe the specter of total war chases him out of his mind and body and time's matrix, until Russian soldiers rescue him. He returns to Dresden years later, if only in imagination.

Perhaps in his 50s he realizes how WWII lends psychic immunity to Americans dropping record-breaking ordnance on Vietnam and Cambodia in the 1960s and '70s. Perhaps as an old man approaching death in the 21st century, he sees how such bombings immunize Americans against revulsion to the Shock and Awe we visited on Iraqis.

Just before bouncing out of his corporeal life, he hears death cries of millions in some future war. Hmmm, is that a mushroom cloud he glimpses exploding there, courtesy of good Christians and Jews and agnostics in Los Alamos and Oak Ridge?

Did I mention Vonnegut is an atheist? That he likes Jesus quite a lot anyhow? Especially the Sermon on the Mount? That he believes kindness is the one gift all should bring to the world? That he rescues his son from insanity and self-medication in the 1970s, nurtures him to wellness with tender love and affection? That he thinks we all could use just a little more socialism? And that war's a terrible idea for people on a finite world grown clever at making bombs? That he writes, "We're addicted to oil" years before the Shrub discovers the convenience of paying lip service to reality? That he knows time is relative?

So it goes.

Vonnegut believes our greatest heroes are altruistic volunteer firefighters and not, say, warriors like Pat Tillman or Jessica Lynch, whom the military-industrial-media machine sought to foist off on us as poster children for the war. Think what a younger Vonnegut might do with such real-life material. The economy he'd bring to showing soldiers in camouflage running out of a hospital carrying Lynch, as if in rescue. Imagine how the writer might pogo his readers across time's checkered kitchen floor to show her riding a tire-swing at age eight, all freckles and curls as she swings round a West Virginia white oak tree and muses on the future. How he'd cut back to show an Iraqi surgeon picking up a phone to call Americans and say, "We've dressed the wounds of one Jessica Lynch. She's leddy to check out now."

Watch Vonnegut bounce back to boot camp, then across time and space to portray Pentagon PR flacks as they tailor the Lynch legend. Watch how they position cameras to record Americans rushing the hospital, guns drawn. Vonnegut might sum up the darkly humorous hero scam as he sums up so much of the world's phony baloney in *Cat's Cradle*, with five little words:

No cat. No cat's cradle.

No Vonnegut? Time forfend. Earlier this century I miss an opportunity to meet him when he speaks at UT. A friend relates his charm, his wit, the story of how he'd recently survived a house fire. Does his admiration of firefighters, best expressed in *God Bless You Mr. Rosewater,* foreshadow this event by 50 years, somehow, or is the reverse true?

Bouncing around my own life's hologram, it's hard to imagine it without Vonnegut. See me in the back of Miss Pearsall's chemistry class reading *God Bless You, Mr. Rosewater*, looking into my own bigotry and closed-mindedness, thanks to Vonnegut's clarifying X-ray vision. I'm 15. I'll devour four more Vonnegut books before I'm 16, and through all the years, I'll see how Vonnegut gets so much right in book before book. I'll thank him for warnings and foreshadowings of heartbreak and wisdom to come. I thank him tomorrow. I thank him yesterday. I thank him now.

God bless you, Mr. Vonnegut.

With love and loss and sad admiration after all these months.

So you go.

New Millennium Writings

Is pleased to present the New Millennium

Poetry Awards

Winning entries appear on pages 143-145 (see Contents pages)

Winter 2007-08

Harry Bauld, New York, NY, *Alaska*

Summer 2007

Ellen Sullins, Tucson, AZ, *The Visible Spectrum*

HONORABLE MENTIONS

Summer 2007	*Winter 2007-08*
Susan Berlin, Yarmouth Port, MA	Ruth Daigon, Corte Madera, CA
Ronda Broatch, Kingston, WA	Merle Feld, Northampton, MA
Patrick Carrington, Wildwood Crest, NJ	Gayle Elen Harvey, Utica, NY
Katherine A. Case, Berkeley, CA	Laura Hilton, Auburn, CA
Mary D. Cole, Gloucester, MA	Wayne Lee, Santa Fe, NM
Barbara de la Cuesta, Beachwood, NJ	Angela Masterson Jones, Terra Ceia, FL
Pamela Ethington, Syracuse, NY	Karla K. Morton, Denton, TX
Diane Gilliam, Akron, OH	Amy Nawrocki, Hamden, CT
Nellie Hill, Berkeley, CA	Suzanne Owens, Littleton, MA
Anthony Hughes, Orchard Park, NY	Mil Norman-Risch, Richmond, VA
Alice Owens Johnson, Black Mtn., NC	Charles Sharpe, Bainbridge Island, WA
Bobbi Dykema Katsanis, Berkeley, CA	Laura Spagnoli, Philadelphia, PA
Pat Landreth Keller, Hawkinsville, GA	Eleanor St. James, Poulsbo, WA
Ellen LaFlèche, Northampton, MA	Nell Stanton, Ithaca, NY
Christina Lovin, Lancaster, KY	Kurt Steinwand, Brandon, FL
Bernard Mann, Austin, TX	Emily Laura Tallman, Oakland, CA
Angella Nazarian, Los Angeles, CA	Dianalee Velie, Newbury, NH
Yvonne Postelle, San Rafael, CA	Jeanne Wagner, Kensington, CA
Michael Sweeney, Shelton, CT	Pamela Wagner, Wethersfield, CT
Alinda Wasner, Lansing, MI	Cynthia West, Santa Fe, NM

For guidelines to our next contest, see page 9

Harry Bauld
Alaska

Before I caught the salmon he caught my eye
in a Kenai stream, a nothing little trickle across the toe
of trail where long grass rustled on my run. I began to sing—
to alert the bear, *Human here,* as if notes could form a name
to protect me from the savage lip,
as if menace were something to shake like a hand.

But there was no bear, only my shaking hand
left over from the bear that stalks the mind's eye.
The rushes still quivered like an actor's lip
and I crept to the trail edge on tip toe
to find like Adam any new creature I could name
in the wilderness, any moving thing whose praise I might sing.

Of harms and this salmon I sing—
a sockeye with a dorsal fin big as my hand
flapping in six inches of puddle no map would bother to name
and wriggling toward home, his enigmatic eye
alight with breed's burden. I could touch it with my toe
and did, saw the fleshy bellows of its hooked lip

open and close in crossbite, a lip
like a kris, like a bow, like an instrument to sing
an aria of longing and return to help me toe
what little line I have been given. I raised my hand,
like a dutiful student or a voter signaling aye.
Then like an animal I forgot my own name,

knelt streamside not in prayer but in the name
of what made him come home. Don't give me any lip
about rainbows, regression, catch and release, an eye for an eye.
I bent close enough to hear what rivers and rushes sing
to a salmon, ear to those changes, my hand
given like a weed to the water, each refracted finger fat as a toe.

Then the ancient current like an undertow
pulled me down into the desire that has no civilized name;
with a bear's trick I scooped him with one hand
and wrestled him to the bank, dug two fingers in his lip
like a hook and heard him soughing what the dead sing,
clubbed him until he went sheet-blank in the eye.

I pushed a stick through his lip and carried him home to sing
to my people of the hunter's eye, to hang him like mistletoe,
our secret names written in the river in my trembling hand.

Ellen Sullins
The Visible Spectrum

'For me, the most rewarding writing often starts out as one thing and morphs into something else entirely. When I began this piece, I was lightheartedly pondering the question of what goes on (or doesn't) in the minds of cats, but then the poem grabbed my pen and the rest of The Visible Spectrum wrote itself. The desire to return to that state of altered consciousness and emotional openness is what keeps me writing.'

~ **Ellen Sullins**

I.
She used to wonder a lot
about what went through the mind
of her old cat Sybil
and once she said to her old friend Jay
wouldn't it be cool to spend a day inside her head
you know to really experience cat
reality and he said hmm maybe not
might make you crazy and even though
that conversation was years ago she still
thinks of it often and wonders if it might be true
that only cats can handle cat consciousness
and if so would it also be true that a cat couldn't
handle human consciousness because maybe
what happened was her dad
was really a cat who somehow landed in a human
body with a human brain and that's why eventually
he had to take that shotgun to obliterate
the consciousness so alien to his essence
but maybe she's reaching a little there.

II.
Or maybe not
because she also daydreams a lot
about waking up with new and improved vision
that would let her see beyond the currently visible
spectrum of light not to make bifocals
unnecessary but allow her to apprehend
the colors hiding in the really really
short and the really really long
undulations because wouldn't it be cool
to experience something as incomprehensible as that
and then she thinks hmm might make her crazy
but then if she did
discover something like maybe
infrared smells like death or birth or maybe ultraviolet
has the texture of Aphrodite's inner labia wouldn't insanity
be a small price to pay and she's reminded
of the people she knows who stopped doing acid
or peyote back in the day
because they knew... the next time
they wouldn't have the will to come back

and all the ones who didn't know
they wouldn't have the will or didn't care
but she's been very fortunate and didn't actually know
any of those.

III.
Although her brother
did sort of loosely fit that category
after Vietnam except it wasn't drug-drugs that got
him though he certainly did plenty of them saying why
should an emotional cripple any more than a physical
cripple have to give up his crutches let alone
his wheelchair and she remembers thinking that he did
have a point but then it turned out to be all the beer
in his bloodstream that day that either fucked
up his judgment or just persuaded him
to go on and blast through the stop sign
where the road dead-ends at the highway
with that big tree on the other side
either way they said he died instantly
and yes she says she's wondered all the clichés
about that last instant of his
and her dad's
like did they see the real and true face of god
in all its holy splendor and all but when she lets
herself imagine the full spectrum of feelings
they might have had then her own
reality begins to shimmer and sway
in a bendy-stretchy kind of way and she has to pull
herself back from even looking
at that land of melting clocks and buzzards
because what distinguishes her from them
might be nothing more than a gene here a peptide there
and even if she's been saved so far by something like the fullness
of two entire X chromosomes you never know
when some little acid-base pair might just wink off or on
and she could very well join the ranks
of the unwilling or unable to come back
from such a place where the entire spectrum of all that is
is visible.

Originally appeared in *The Moon*; reprinted in *Elsewhere (Plan B Press, 2007)*
More by Ellen Sullins, next page

Ellen Sullins
Homage To A Red Honda Civic

You haven't
really plumbed the potential of your psyche until
you've driven across country alone at the end
of another affair, especially if you're driving the little
red Honda you bought in '77 with the drab
of divorce money sticky with guilt and bright promise,
this car like a red metal womb that six years later has proven
more steadfast than any of the cast of characters
hitchhiking across your heart—a few months here
a year or two there—before one of you says "This
is as far as I go" and it's you and the Honda again.

Like now
heading west out of New Orleans with the sun
slipping toward the horizon and the road behind you
stretched out like a fat rubber band attached to your bumper
and stubbornly anchored to the man who most likely
is still sitting in that bar in The Quarter, the one
where the house drink is called a Climax so you
ordered a double and he said *mmm-hmm*, even now
the Honda pushes ahead, the little-engine-that-could,
doing its best to soothe and distract you with music
that conjures imaginary lovers riding in the passenger's seat.

Like the one
that appears just now as you cross into Texas,
the rubber band's pull overwhelming and the Honda
choosing Dire Straits to remind you (*everybody's got a knife,
it can be just what they want it to be*) and there he is,
pushing back his seat the better to unfurl those lanky legs he knows
you're a sucker for, and he cocks his head to look you over
with half-veiled eyes and a little Rorschach smile that says
oh honey, a double climax wouldn't even begin to describe it.

And hours later
when that one has been exhausted and your right leg
no longer seems attached to your body and the night
is the bottom of an ocean where your headlights reveal
ghostly blind creatures swimming across the road
and one is clearly the cat that was put to sleep
when you were ten, the Honda comes to your rescue again
with Miles and Coltrane blowing *So What,* and beside you
appears the one who wants nothing more in life than to hear
your thoughts on Miles and Basquiat and Clapton and Ginsberg
and Hegel and god and whether or not Hegel is god, and even
your treatise on the tragedy of Steely Dan disbanding, and although
he asks you many probing questions, in the end he usually
concedes the point and always admires your tenacity.

And just
when it seems like months you've been driving through Texas,
and the passenger seat holds only your purse and beef jerky
wrappers and a few thousand crumpled cigarette packs, fresh
caffeine starts percolating across your synapses and the rear
view mirror fills with the lemony light of morning, and at last
the Honda reaches escape velocity, the rubber band snapping
out of its mooring, launching you free of the pull of the earth,
and you float like a capsule in space on a graceful trajectory toward
some new promise, not merely away from your old familiar songs.

Homage to a Red Honda Civic first appeared in Concho River Review and in Elsewhere (Plan B Press, 2007). Degrees of Freedom, next page, first appeared in Carquinez Poetry Review and in Elsewhere (Plan B Press, 2007).

Ellen Sullins

Degrees of Freedom

after Bruce Snider's 'The Certainty of Numbers'

It isn't the numbers you love
—the roots and sines and logs—
it's the way the answers are always
      so definite
there's no real need for a You.
It's how 2 plus 3 is always 5, never
8 or 9 or your family. That anything
divided by N minus 1 does not
require an opinion on global affairs,
and negative times negative is positive,
not like your brother times brother or father.
How the sum of X-squared is clearly
so different from the sum of X, squared
      and neither is ever
your own critique of Existentialism
swaying in the breeze, a possibly empty
piñata dodging the big theory stick They
swing. And formulas! Benevolent maps
that guide you away from your father's despair
and your own. The autistic escape of 5 and 6 and
leave the sticks and stones and certainly the words
alone—7 times 7 the stairway to heaven, which
happens to equal the inverse of home.

* *How to Read a Poem: Beginner's Manual, is scheduled for publication in Pamela's new book, We Mad Climb Shaky Ladders (CavanKerry Press, 2009).*

Pamela Spiro Wagner
How to Read a Poem: Beginner's Manual *

First, forget everything you have learned,
that poetry is difficult,
that it cannot be appreciated by the likes of you,
with your high school equivalency diploma,
your steel-tipped boots,
or your white-collar misunderstandings.

Do not assume meanings hidden from you:
the best poems mean what they say and say it.

To read poetry requires only courage
enough to leap from the edge
and trust.

Treat a poem like dirt,
humus rich and heavy from the garden.
Later it will become the fat tomatoes
and golden squash piled high upon your kitchen table.

Poetry demands surrender,
language saying what is true,
doing holy things to the ordinary.

Read just one poem a day.
Someday a book of poems may open in your hands
like a daffodil offering its cup
to the sun.

When you can name five poets
without including Bob Dylan,
when you exceed your quota
and don't even notice,
close this manual.

Congratulations.
You can now read poetry.

Pamela Spiro Wagner
The prayers of the mathematician...

rise without sound,
primes uttered like a rosary's
beaded polynomials of devotion,
climbing the sky towards a god
unknowable as the dark infinity
between rational and irrational
numbers. His hair in a wild corona
framing eyes so deep-set
they seem to drown what's caught there,
knowing the hardest questions
may sometimes answer,
he wanders the halls
pale and abstracted as pi,
trailing numbers in chalkdust,
like the spectral footprints of a ghost
no one remembers passing there,
these incandescents of his faith
illuminating all the unsayables
as only equations can,
in brief yellow chalk on a green board:
that life yearns towards binariness,
that our ending is in our beginning,
that if we name as nouns
the verbs he numbers in strictest silence,
our dualism's just as binary:
good or evil, pure or profane,
we only constrain what he sets free
with his meticulous 1's,
his careful and perfect 0's.

The mathematician referenced here is the troubled Nobel Prize-winner John Nash before A Beautiful Mind won him popular acclaim. This poem won first place in the 2001 02 international poetry contest sponsored by the BBC World Service and is scheduled for publication in Pamela's new book, We Mad Climb Shaky Ladders (CavanKerry Press, 2009).

Eleanor St. James
Half Flight

Underneath your skin
you are a swallowtail butterfly
regal, feebly fluttering
with one magnificent, fragile wing.
How I long for you to sip sweet nectar,
to lose yourself in the heady fragrance
of wild hyssop blooms.
I will spare part of life looking for wings.
I will look in gutters before rain comes.
I will hunt dark, neglected corners where
things like discarded wings mound up.
And when I find your wing,
my golden swallowtail,
I will gently cup you
in my hands,
stroke your downy hair
in one direction,
and lift
your missing wing
into place,
saddened
by the years
it will take you
to learn
how
to fly.

Katherine Case
Life of the Giant Squid

She propels herself through infinite space using a long
series of sighs, muscled arms pumping tandem ballet

in the half light. She may never see another of her kind,
may never be a mother, might not be glimpsed

by a passing ship or deep-roving submarine as she swims
at unknown speeds through water spotted with phytoplankton,

oil-thick and cloudy, while the massive, slanted remnants of daylight
fade down into darkness. *What else to do.* She speeds up,

bits of plant life streak by like comets or stars, and she opens
her beak, relaxes her belly and feels for a moment

the life of the ocean coursing through. At rest, constellations of algae
sway slowly in near space, oppressive in their benign totality

like that great bowl of humid air resting over the plains of Illinois
on a cloudy day—a world belted by the horizon.

She keeps moving, and again the day ends. Light removes itself
from water, and speed and direction are chosen now not by vision

or distance but by the bleak geometry of curved bottom, invisible horizon,
the eventual return of color, until which she is a planet hurtling

through uncharted space, her huge eyes mirror back the black
of water as it passes, her almost-companion in the quiet dark.

Doppelganger

We rearranged the furniture, cleaned the fish tank
and moved it to the hall table near the bathroom, where now

of our three old goldfish—tennis-ball sized ancients whose cheek sacs
sag around their raggedy fins—one has taken to watching me

as I get ready in the morning or at night, walking past in slippers
and an old t-shirt, so that when the tank is the only light

and train noises come soft through the open window
I think of his lidless dog-eyes or catch myself looking again

toward the hallway out the open bedroom door. What is this
I cannot admit? If I am nothing more

than a huge, ill-defined shadow not of his fear,
but of all the things he could not possibly know,

passing with a coffee cup most mornings just when the sun
almost reaches the far corner of his green haze, then how is it

for the mundane clockwork of this life to be his liminal world,
a parallel universe in which nothing happens, in which I leave the apartment

every morning, stand on the stairs in the sunshine, look up
and still don't notice the darkness beyond my own blue sky.

Karla K. Morton
Dilation

Driving back from the eye doctor,
dusk turned to dark,
and as I pulled in to park, I became feline.

I slinked out of the truck to sit on the stoop,
looking up through two pupils
huge and dark with dilation;

understanding my cat's
wild fascination with the night;
how every pinpoint of light became starred and feathered;

not knowing whether Moon was orb or Goddess
in her silver broad headdress of halo—
her undeniable undertow of magic.

How tragic that humans don't know this world,
where the beasties and flowers are glistened and pearled,
and all is lost to the night... Ah, but one time, I knew...

and now my cat looks back as she passes out the door,
to the dark once more... with eyes, wild and wide—
the Goddess, calling, calling, calling her outside.

Angela Masterson Jones
First Taste of War

for Randy Masterson

You sprang from your nap on the floor
when I kissed you, in your thin ribbed
undershirt with armholes bigger than my head.
Supper, Mom had said.
Go wake your dad.

I didn't know I'd find you
on hills of high grass,
rifle slung over khaki shoulder,
swinging to the beat of dry-socked,
booted feet, following a cadence
called by countrymen
in a foreign land.

Korea was not a place I'd met,
at seven, because I hadn't yet seen
how it made you lunge,
alarm camouflaged in sleep
by twitching eyelids, ticking cheeks.

I got my first taste of war in that kiss,
my baby tooth's loose root
knocked free by the strong
bone of your chin
that quivered at supper when I couldn't eat
because of all our blood
on my lips.

Wayne Lee
My Father's War

For Henry David Esau, 1913-1997

Life is perfect.
My father is five years old,
youngest son of a Mennonite pastor
in this quiet Ukrainian village.

This is before the Revolution.
Before the wounded soldiers appear at the door.
Before the children start finding bodies in the field.
Before the family is reduced to eating garbage.
Before the Bolsheviks march their horses
like shining toys across the Steppes.

Before the family flees by train to Estonia,
by boat to England, by ship to Canada.
Before they become outsiders in a Protestant land.
Long before World War II, when my father joins
the RCAF, trains airmen to take off and never return,
gets reassigned to a German POW camp in Alberta,
exchanges drawings, jokes and smokes with prisoners
just as lost as he.

This is before I am born.

It is a perfect day,
a cloudless, windless, summer day.
Everyone at work in the fields, the kitchens, the barns.
Amid the gentle sounds of their labors,
a distant buzz like a mosquito in the next room.
Then a biplane, weaving its way erratically
above the squares of rye and wheat,
banking over the schoolhouse and church,
circling the cows grazing in the paddock,
casting a shadow like a giant hawk.

Now they see the pilot, flying low, flying crazy,
goggles askew, scaring the chickens and ducks,
setting the dogs barking, stopping the workers in mid-task,
steering with one gloved hand, reaching inside the cockpit
with the other, pulling something up, holding something out,
dropping something down, watching something fall toward the herd,
explode like thunder at their feet, send smoke and sod and pieces of cow
like fireworks spiraling through the morning air, the biplane arcing,
jerking, diving like a rabid bird of prey, the pilot reaching again
inside his cockpit, holding out again that instrument of death,
dropping again that terrible bomb, reaching, holding, dropping, watching
again and again and again until the detonations stop, the air stills,
the mouths close, the tears spill, till every single cow lies shattered
as the morning calm.

Some say they heard the pilot laugh as he banked and sputtered away
like a hacking drunk back from where he came.

Life is perfect.
My father is dead,
years after quitting booze, leaving wives
and children, abandoning art and giving up on life.
It simply made no sense to him, the death, the insanity,
the slaughter of innocents on the golden fields of his youth.

He never forgot the cows, couldn't shake the specter
of that drunken bomber, couldn't abide that shell-shocked exit
from childhood. For my father stood among the herd that day,
did not survive beyond the perfect age of five.

Diane Gilliam *(for Daddy)*
Your pencil breaks...

... as you try to write the poem you are meaning
to write. One more reason to give up, go
downstairs and start a pot of coffee. But you like

the electric sharpener, so you heft
yourself up out of the couch and head across
the room for the desk. You remember the metal

sharpener bolted to the back wall in Room 5
and how you had to raise your hand for permission.
Broken lead's grist for that noisy mill, the half-wood,

half-metal smell of it. How the broken black bone
of the pencil came out sanded and smooth,
ready to yield its point to whatever

you wanted to write. You remember
homework and the round kitchen table and only
one pencil in the house. Your father's hands—

his fingers trembling from overwork—dangle
over the trashcan, broken pencil
in his left hand, kitchen knife in his right,

its blade flat against the pad of his thumb,
whittling at the point. How the shavings
fell unshaped and thick, the lead not long

and cylindrical now, but nub-shaped
like something out of his toolbox. Even the tip
slightly squared off so that the up-and-down lines

of your letters come out too thick, the sideways curves
way too thin—the odd, homely calligraphy
of his rough edges shaping all your words.

Your Pencil Breaks first appeared in Appalachian Heritage.

Gayle Elen Harvey
Among All Instruments

In some other life, perhaps, you were an oboe,
cor anglaise, transposing instrument, and I, Sumerian lyre, plucked
bare-fingered, just as now, tonight,
clasped taut against your belly, your hands are transposing me,
my breasts, my guarded thighs strummed lentamente, to arpeggios
of wanting. Dolce—
Dolcemente, you bring both of us to perfect pitch.

Among all instruments, you were, perhaps, a contra bass,
flesh polished rosewood in this votive light,
your potent, thrumming curves a skyline, harbor like Marseilles
or Istanbul at nightfall, mosqued and sonorous
with its muezzin.

Within this life, I've come to you, impaired, debauched with
sorrow, but you keep time, play rubato, lingering,
tenendo, giving, taking until I become wind instrument, recorder,
swart interior receiving you,
your carillon of grace notes filling me until, felice, svgliando,
I can't make a sound.

Patrick Carrington
A Heraldry of Hands

I've always been taken by women's hands,
each with their own way of being
in history. But I'm untouched
by the ones satiny with birthrights
and a pinky raised for tea. I'm
never sure what to make of hands
like those, the purchased purity
as spotless as new linens,
lifelines like the seam
of untroubled glass. They are

so unlike hands of earned identity
that are more soul than skin,
that bear damage,
the blemishes and bends that say
earth is not a place of justice,
that wear a simple ring so well
union really does seem sacred. As a boy

I was fascinated by my grandmother's,
how her hands were a human story
written at Hardscrabble Creek
in knobs and nicks, in slants
that spoke celery snaps of bones,
cottonfields and crazy days. I listened,

and they told me hands were made
before spades, and I could hear
the wail of slaves
as they dug with crooked fingers,
the sobs of mourners
muffled in palms as dirt was turned.

And too, I heard better times. Crackle
of ice they held in enough highballs
for her to miss a few trains and steps,
the secrets in the silky rub
of rented rooms. They said years

are pushed down hard by rain,
and in the mud I could tell
without looking at her face
how beautiful she must have been
in a storm. Her hands were clean

because she had wept on them so oft
and marked fields and flesh
with their chaste blood. I stared
until I wanted to grow up clutching
such beauty and scars to me,
closer than any love or tattoo.

*A Heraldry of Hands first appeared in
The Evansville Review.*

Mil Norman-Risch
Song

whether a dog sleeps too much
or whether he just sleeps

(like saying "this pot boils too much"
or "this hand holds too much"
or "this heart feels too much")

the dog just sleeps

the hand holds

the pot boils

why ask

whether there is too much suffering

four gray birds on a limb
sing and sing and sing and sing

and somewhere the blinds are closed
and somewhere the sidewalk is in the shadow of an elm
and somewhere long rafters in a barn are hung with ropes

empty
but not too empty.

Vicki Goodfellow Duke
Garment

'Suppose time is a circle, bending back on itself.'
—**Alan Lightman**

The gown
is fairy-pleated
in damask silk,
bodice formed
to the waist's curve,
firm in the long groove
of your back.
See how chiffon falls
over the contour of hips,
fluted sleeves
grazing the wrist.
Note the well-placed pearl,
each hand-culled bead.

Turn once, and look
through this gossamer veil
back to the bend
in the circle.
See the circumference
of your life,
the way the hours curl
in a ring from then to now
and begin over,
each wound as hook and eye,
binding the fabric of days.
How in going round
you would not alter
one scar, embroidered
seamless,
the glossed brilliance
of completion.

Falling Dark

The flower seller in a fringed wool shawl,
a scarcity of berries and summer squash. The little things
you hardly notice. Cathedral doors locked after Matins,
the scent of musk, over lavender and pear.
And one day you look
and your father is old, the streets bare,
dark turned in, and you know the permissions
you give yourself, in a city settling
with snow, you can't remember falling.

Amy Wright
The Part of the Universe That Looks at Itself

> *'Sometimes a single phrase is like a lion*
> *crouching on the ground.'* —Yuan-Wu

through isinglass of air
a small motion slows
inside the bellows
of the body, an aperture
in the evergreens "for love
I am contingent"
on the Gelvie looking back
eyes black as drains. The clear
open space between two things
The calf is being pulled out
by a man through the pupil
toward the question
of boundary. I end
where you begin
only sometimes
in the snap of hair, the tips
glisten in all directions
& there is no place
we can remain
separate selves

Ruth Daigon
The Drowning

1.
We keep pulling him up
from the bottom of the Red River
in stop-action or slow-motion
and replay the splash
Blooming around his hips.

We correct his dive
restore the promise
of his form each movement clear
in the instant of falling.

The moment reversed
we reel him up
to where he's still
sitting on the bank.

Mother covers
her bare scalp with hair
torn by its roots

Scream sucked back
become soft
syllables again.

Her shredded clothes
re-woven. The table set
for his return.

2.
Again he's swimming
and the Red River
takes him in.

Mother's rooted to the bank
her voice floating over water.
We're waiting supper for you.

Bread and milk lie
heavy on the table where sisters
stand strange to one another

They turn their backs
and climb the stairs
to narrow rooms.

It's that time of year
nudging memories of
his face streaked with summer

murmurs at evening meals
walks along the river
with its glowing spine.

In this house where
no one survives love
darkness opens like a white door.

3.
Summer nights we'd sit on the back veranda
planing down the hours with small talk.
Stories flowed in a spill of old pleasures,
sweet and tart and light on the tongue.
The air was fresh, the weather excellent.
The room radiant with the dead.

Laura Hilton
Drowning

as the car wills itself
into summer dark
and a waiting midnight river
she remembers
this crazed flight—
the sinking of metal
the weight of water

and so she is prepared
she knows what to do
which is to release the harness
it is so easy
this first part
and she is confident

but she hasn't dreamt the black of it
how could she?
at the end
which is now
there are no colors
no lines
and she acknowledges
even accepts
that she has forgotten the next step

Yvonne Postelle
Journey

*'When I talk of a trip I mean
forever,'* —**Adrienne Rich**

To float day after day
on a broad river
into whatever comes after—
as the early Americans
are said to have done—
seems not the worst way;

to follow the river's bend,
slowly separating
from the known
letting the carved canoe,
with its scant provision
of dried maize, wend
toward a greater water
where no one
has seen the end;

to give oneself
to the journey
the way the arctic tern must
when it begins its long flight
to a dimly remembered spot,
sensing the direction
one wing beat at a time;

to travel night
after star-lit night
until you get there,
until you're gone.

Merle Feld

Aunt Julie In Our Doorway

Making fun of Aunt Julie was a family sport,
her wide open face beckoning like a target,
the large twin circles of her spectacles
forming a double bullseye, offering no protection
to the pale watery eyes behind them, eyes
that seemed perpetually surprised by the casual cruelties
of her siblings and their spouses, perpetually
surprised that even their well-brought up children
finally couldn't bring themselves to laugh
along with her as she laughed and laughed.

Hers was a distinctive laugh, like a small summer
waterfall, little peals and gales, falling and falling
and then starting at the top all over again.
A gay laugh, a child's laugh, a laugh from high
in the throat, she laughed as if she had no
alternative, as if laughter and confusion were all
that God had given her to choose from.

And then at the end of every visit, Aunt Julie
in our doorway. It's common to describe someone
as "lingering in the doorway," but that's not it at all—
Aunt Julie took up residence in the doorway,
planted herself there and effectively resisted
any effort to uproot her. This too, of course,
became a set piece when riffing on the peculiarities
of Aunt Julie—Aunt Julie and her long goodbyes.

How far a journey was it after all—
three city blocks to her own small apartment,
back to the coarse widower who had taken her
for wife, taken her to wash his underwear, mind
his daughter, scrub the linoleum, have supper
on the table. Fifty years later I wake up remembering
and finally understand: *There's something
I came for and didn't get, something I need.*
So hard to leave without it.

Jeanne Wagner
Photo of You Taken by the 'Other Woman'

Brighton Beach, 2006

I like the way the scene seems to smear,
as if shot through the rainy windscreen of a car,
and the way you're caught
turning away from the bleary distance,
indifferent as a child
taking a back-seat to everything outside,
while inside
he listens to the wipers' metronomic rhythm,
the warm exhalations of a heater kicking in,
making him playful in a callous way,
as you are now,
standing under a red umbrella.

Now that I think of it, you seem dressed
a bit too formally,
considering what sort of day it is,
those natty black slacks
not even covered by an anorak,
and the slight back-heel tilt of your body,
the way it's casually swaying
to a music I can't hear,
as if you're singing,
just singing in the rain.

And of course the pier
functions mostly as a prop,
symbol of how heartlessly things burn
when untended:
the old pavilion melting like a movie vampire
when the light of dawn overtakes his face,
though yours will remain
hidden behind that red umbrella,
which is complicit here,
flaring like a struck match, so tense
I can almost hear it hiss and arch its back
against the rain.

Pat Landreth Keller
Draglines *

twins   the ones she told us were murdered
floated through the telling so many times

she believed she saw them dragged to the river's flat surface
that calm spring day   barbed wire for collars

twelve   she said   pretty little girls
tossing slippers and stockings up the sandy bank

tucking hems into their bloomers   wading the shallows
at the cowpath's end   water lapping the willows

barehanded man whipping wire into lassoes
spinning those girls like sugar   tied back to back

2.
shuffling old man   thick-tongued   sad
coins sticky in his open hand
Her seeing wanting

she said he tried to kiss her   she said
she tried not to think of twins two weeks in the water
strung together like beads

silver spilling from his fingers
he said   *closer*
hand under her dress   she said like water rising

she felt his tongue each time
she slipped a hidden nickel from under the shaving soap
her papa left behind   she said if she dropped the nickel

the old man's words rolled under the door
gotta little honey by the stockyard   comes to my room
likes my hand on her   sweet little leg

she said she'd kept the taste of metal on her tongue
fingerprints on her thigh   old as she was
said the twins never would quit turning in her mind

washing into the river   out of the river
hair tangled in the willows
just like wanting   she said   just like words

Independence Day

I have wanted it forever—
now it is mine,
your fur from the war years:
ripped lining, frazzled seams,
hem snagged in a car door's sudden slam
behind a beer joint on the river road;

rubbed hairless around a collar
turned up high for careening, breakneck rides
over rutted ice to rough backwater camps;
split up the sleeve
you raised, your loose and happy arm
saluting the moon;

matted,
a smell like last year's rum-soaked cake;
pockets bulged outward from long-gone bottles of gin;
cuffs tattooed by drifting cigarettes;
frayed belt, lost buttons,
lipstick stains.

It is all the style you had.
It is all your sons remember from those nights
huddled in the backseat as you leaned
on whatever man was driving you home at closing:
they felt it gather and climb your moonlit thighs
as his slow hand moved.

Now it is mine:
Mine the barrel, the kindling, the gasoline,
the flame:
ashes for my brothers, who learned to weep
at the sound of hinges, who wept each time
you tossed it back over the seat to comfort them.

* *A slightly different version of Draglines appeared in GSU Review and is the
title poem in a forthcoming chapbook from Toadlily Press.*

Laura Spagnoli

Nest

First what would save me: red kettle,
wooden crate, the spoon, knife and fork
in a drawer.

There's enough light to read by the window
eye-level with what moves away:
pigeons, chimney smoke,
other eyes looking out
for other things.

The message I write says *I'm fine.* Still warm
in the gray coat a man gave me. Still young
enough. Still pretty. I push my way in
to subway cars crammed with shopping bags and hands.
I slip into galleries, restaurants, apartments
like the mice I will have to kill
in this new kitchen
when they come in.

What cracks we find in hard things—
fissured concrete and brickwork, a nickel-size breach
where the tiles meet the stairs.
Pink nose sniffs the hole by a heating pipe.
Now another gets in, you see?

Hungry still, they make doors
beside doors that are shut. In the dark,
on all fours—what they must, what I must—
that one so low she fits, lucky thing.

Lucky me on the floor I call my own floor,
safe enough to tell lies—I am nothing
like them—even down on my knees by this trap
that's caught another one,
scratching slow, half alive.

The one that has me playing which-way-is-worse,
putting one hand over my eyes.
The head I smash in *to be kind*
with my other hand
in a shoe.

Charles Sharpe
The good old boys
in my closet...

play mumbledy-peg
and rock paper scissors
with their long bony fingers
and they bicker in the dark.

Their names are Mr. Jim,
Crackers, Hum Bow, Karma,
Slick and Uncle Shiva
and they sit on milk crates
clicking and clacking their teeth

drinking beer with saltines
and pickled herring,
banging and thumping around
when they get bored.

They scrape and wheeze,
singing sea chanteys
when Crackers plays his concertina
and they turn the vacuum on and off
and put on my hats and shoes
just to laugh at themselves.

But when I can't hear them,
I become nervous
and wonder what they're up to.

They wait quietly for me
so I'll forget they're there
and open the door—
they stand and drool
and leer at my friends while Mr. Jim
makes rhymes about my past.

When I've been away,
they wait anxiously,
pressing their ears to the door
hoping I'll feel sorry for them
and let them out
to clatter about opening
cupboards and drawers
as if they were memories.

If I'm not minding them
they shamble into the street
led by Uncle Shiva,
playing their snare drum
and turning over garbage cans,
singing folk songs
late into the night.

Hum Bow and Slick break
into neighbor's garages
to steal paint so they can write
things about me in large letters
on the street,
resisting like drunk uncles
my furtive attempts
to round them up
and get them back
into the closet—
where they belong.

Dianalee Velie
Love All

Poets have to love a game beginning
Love/All, Forty/Love, so close to winning,

the lack of a point signified by Love
under unconditional skies above.

Admiring your backhand return, I
stare at the ballistic ball transfixed by

its perfect placement in the left corner,
bouncing hard and out of my reach, cleaner

than a slice of life. Such perfection in
motion, I do not run or try to win

this point. It is enough to watch the ball,
like a plunging sun, radiant downfall

of perfection and glory. Awaiting
another return, I bend low, fearing

I have misplaced my competitive edge
with an artist's eye and a poet's pledge

to love all beauty with intensity,
and honor ideal synchronicity,

to honor in verse, with this clear blue sky,
that holy shot, so it will never die.

Rebekah McCarroll
Wonder

Where were you my loving friend
Ever so long ago?
Were we both in the same universe?
Did we have nowhere to go?
Did Venus cradle you to sleep?
Did Mars greet me "hello"?
Where were you my dear friend
So many years ago?

Were your eyes as blue as a hemisphere
Not even yet created?
Was your hair as black as the coal
Wherein diamonds for me awaited?
Were your lips as soft as buttered moon rays
Was your being close to mine?
Where were you my treasured friend
In that long forgotten time?

Did you dance a circle game with me
Around on Jupiter's rings?
Did you play marbles with the stars
Did you hear an angel sing?
Did you know that I was there
Did you ever see my shadow?
Or were our worlds too far apart
That to you it did not matter?

Where were you my beloved friend
Oh so long ago?
Were we ever even up there?
Will we ever really know?
Did black holes of future sin
Ever enter our pure souls?
Were we ever ever up there
So many years ago?

Wonder first appeared in Eva magazine.

Emily Tallman
I Ask My Father About Vietnam

He tells me about the boy
he passed on the dirt road of some nameless village,
on his way to a military hospital.
The boy was alone, walking in an unblinking daze.
His stomach had been blown open.
Someone must have helped him pull the hanging flap of skin,
stretching impossibly from his belly up
between his teeth so he could bite it,
and hold his intestines in.
He was alone and my father
rode past him in the back of a dusty truck,
toward the hospital that would repair his own burns
and send him home.

He stares straight ahead,
sitting at his potter's wheel
and to avoid seeing him cry I stare at his hands,
fingers cracked from the clay
which draws all moisture out as he shapes it.
Sometimes his hands get worn down
where they rub the turning shape until they bleed,
and he keeps working,
blood mixing with the clay.
He leans over the wheel
studying the shape only he can see,
pressing the edges, carefully lifting up,
and I wonder what he is thinking
as he pushes the wetness into a form—
does he see in this spinning
a dirt road? A village?
A boy
with a halo of singed hair
who stumbles, alone,
arms held out from his burned sides
as he bites his own skin,
trying to keep himself from falling out
trying to keep himself *in.*

*I Ask My Father About Vietnam first appeared online,
in Blood Orange Review, Volume 2.2 April 2007.*

Amy Nawrocki
How to Visit Your Alma Mater

It should be quiet when you visit:
choose study days or weekends when students
filter out of dormitory shells in soundless trickles,
ensuring an eerie solitude you'll recognize
as the lonely thump of acorns outside
the dorm room when your parents drove away.

It must be autumn: pine needles crinkle
under feet walking from the parking lot
to campus as the movie of your life
flashes back, each image framed
in an old October light. Red-haired
girls saunter down the same sidewalks
where new buildings startle you.
Think of them as the growth and maturation
you were promised during those first days,
when another autumn felt crisp
as the unbroken binding of a textbook.

Take the boyfriend you dreamed of and show him
the nooks you crannied into: your first classroom
where the discovery of Sappho and Rilke
saved your life not once, but again
and again each time winter clouds
recycled their white pages into spring rain
and you scurried under words for shelter.

When the man you plan to marry
enters you in a library study room,
the nuances and doom of pixie girlhood
disappear as new myths are created,
ones where dreaming no longer aches,
but permeates like red maple sunshine
on your wise and blissful face.

Kurt Steinwand

Tintype

From a photo of my grandparents in a
New 1928 Whippet Roadster, Toledo, OH.

The hired hands were alcoholics,
and beer runners into Ontario—
among them my grandfather
who swerved his Whippet into a pond.

I pull him out
of the picture, the water, the unlit past.
He was a happy drunk until
at Buster's speakeasy *(pull him out, at last)*
on a payday afternoon
he drank himself into a bad dream

about anything and nothing *(dreams*
come and go), too drunk to know or care
about a mad octopus swinging crowbars,
then the bars became scolding crows.

He was only dreaming,
stoned at the edge of a pond of vomit,
awakened to the wounded cursing
of what he thought was an angel . . .
her name was Violet *(my great aunt)*.

His chrome-bright smile,
his brushed-tweed hair...
the tintype doesn't do him justice,
doesn't show the airbrushed layers
of cool Northwest Ohio evenings
in the Whippet driving him onward.

Violet turtled into the rumble seat.
They took off down Statesville Road
to Buster's *(pull them out, and fast)*,

with grins like gleaming radiator grills.
They split the wheat on either side,
feeling their oats and gulping the grain.

After crashing *(and stashing the hootch)*,
he flagged a mule team, hauled the car out,
beat the front of the fender smooth
the best he could by Sunday morning
where he spilled the offertory wine sloppily
in front of the priest at St. Joe's church.

The Whippet sat in rutted mud
with the black Tin Lizzies of the working men
(Amen, brethren) as he knelt in the family pew
tinted green from withdrawals and stained glass

...praying for Violet *(which means faithfulness)*
who'd taken a turn for the worse—pneumonia,
puss in the lungs from riding in the rumble seat
and standing garters-deep in cold water,
slapping him awake with her screams
as he smiled and dreamed of the octopus.

They called the Lucas County doctor . . .
eased her onto the kitchen table,
slipped her head onto a pillow of cock feathers.
Three days out she turned the color of her name
and died at the fragile age of seventeen.

It was early spring, the year of The Crash,
and they were to marry in the summer,
but dreams crashed like a hidden hemorrhage,
like the spring beneath its cloth of green
(you'd never know there were ruts in the mud).

Tintype, **continued on p. 178**, *previously appeared online in Riverbabble.*

So Belle, the eldest *(my grandmother)*
left the wake early, boastful, confident,
claiming to know how to care for a man
with a daredevil smile and a car like that.
She was the second-choice, second-best sister
who vowed to fix his damaged love.

Cl-*ap!* goes the tintype at Spielbusch Market,
goes the youth of my grandfather
shirtless behind the wheel, a roll-your-own
centered in a smile big as Al Jolson's,
my grandmother's young and bonneted face
peering out from the rumble seat.

She was thrilled to ride to the picture show
at the Paramount downtown *(talkies were a gas!)*
across from LaSalle's Department Store,
was thrilled as the wind unraveled her ribbons
in the Whippet driving them onward.

Nell Stanton
The Cherry Pie

Out by your pool I pit for hours, lamely
hunched over twin buckets. My hands rusty,
bare legs daubed, at six I slope up to the house.
You point to lemon to take out the stain.
We collaborate nicely on the crust.
Then off to the cold beach, quarrelling, to joust
in black sand under bright firework fields.
Back home, hungry for truce, we turn the key.
The timer chimes, the stainless oven yields
our basted berries, now beached garnet peas.
A wisp of smoke eddies, we flush pink,
stare at our mitts, then a bitterness
like ash or accusation moves between
us, sour bleeding through its latticework screen.

Barbara de la Cuesta
'The Liberation of the Peon'—Diego Rivera

They form a circle round him and
round are the guerilla's faces
and the sombreros, round...
Circlets of bullets crisscross their chests
and pistols ride on hefty buttocks
Round and wild are the horses' eyes
and a lasso holds them
earthbound

They cover the clay colored
body on the ground
with a ruddy blanket
No *Acensión del Señor de Alba* here,
but only a return to earth
under the red
petal of a blanket

Suzanne Owens
Being Watched Outside The Winter Palace
(from the larger work, 'Ten Days In Russia: 1992')

for my son Cullen Owens

Sitting cross-legged on the ground by the bus,
I decide I may as well
barter too.

For a few packs of cigarettes, for a few
American dollars, everywhere we go: in the field
by our hotel, by the back canals,

when we stop in small towns, I witness
young Russian men trading
black market army watches: as cheap

as the candles we lit for the dead
or the few coins we parted with
for penance.

A young vendor pulls up his sleeve, extends
his arm down to me where the watches coil
like a cobra tamed.

Does that one run, does this one
need a battery? He pulls a watch off his arm.
The watch goes from his hand

into mine. Our fingers touch. In a moment
I see the watch in my hand, look up, there
in that space between

the vendor and the clock tower
beyond, the approach
of two gray uniforms...

As they haul him a few yards away,
the other vendors scatter into
the crowds of Leningrad Square.

The billy club snaps
down and down
and down on the young man's skull...

The noise ricochets like shots
off the portals of cathedrals; half conscious,
he keeps on fighting while my own body

seems to be flying away from me; I think
that boy will never
fall, and I want him

to fall, to fall
quickly; through an eternity he falls
he falls the way a leaf does; finally

his body touches the pavement, as softly
as a kiss touches
the closed mouth of an indifferent lover.

His arms and legs flung out, scrawl an X
on the stones;
stomach up he is all exposed

to the sky,
the passersby
and the young policeman who

nods, half smiles over at us,
over a silence into which any
thick-toothed boot might stomp.

Gindy Elizabeth Houston
Postpain

for Cecilia Woloch

This poem bled an awful
red—revision's cuts
tore what I'd knit past limits
of the alphabet.
Seeping like another lovelorn
kitchen tap, it wept in shapeless vowels.
Weeping too, I let
my hand speak in my voice's stead:

Dear poem, it said, *this pain you weather
is not yours, but mine.*

Now this poem rests. Mends.
A new wound opens,
my own door to anchored ends—
wound of loss and closure, thief of
my found rapture—
one more grief that,
like a shadow, panthers after.

Poem to be Read Aloud by Its Author

This is not disaster

Or it shouldn't be   By the time I start
reading I'll have a sense
an intuition of something ready to go wrong

Frightening how I feel every reading
will be my last   Meanwhile Rwandan refugees
who *survived* the 1994 genocide

(I write again   who *survived)*
suffer from HIV and AIDS
as a result of violence

What's one person in a population
one person in statistics   all it takes
to murder   all it takes to read a poem

if I never make it to the next line

this is not disaster

Angella M. Nazarian
Glints

The night ocean
shimmers with glinting light.
The moon,
hanging in the velvet darkness,
pours into me and
I forget the way I've been,
the circular life
of unspecified desires,
and the listlessness.

The moon has diminished herself.
She has retreated from the sun
to be in the company of many stars.
She stays up all night to greet the sun.

This is not a night on the calendar.
It's a night beyond the mosaic of imagination,
a night that dissolves through the edge of time
and cascades into an ocean of picturings and pulses.

The turning of the stars,
the breathing galaxies,
the lift and the falling away,
draws me near to the moon.

When I feel this way,
thoughts
even I
don't make sense.

Mary Cole
What It Was

What a big thing,
to sit with secrets,
to have a life beneath your life
that runs with an engine of its own,
fueled by passions unspoken
but leaked out,
like light behind closed doors
flooding through the cracks
and little spaces
where the wood is warped—
so seductive—
gold spilling around the edges
of conversations,
creeping silently

into our curious lives.
As children, we used to think
the trees kept secrets every spring
because we watched so
carefully, to catch them popping into leaf.
But every year the trees fooled us,
dazzling us with displays of green, exactly
when our backs were turned.
We missed the whole scene!
We weren't fast enough,
or maybe
we just weren't paying attention.
My mother had a secret

that she took to her grave.
This secret was a different kind of engine
rumbling underneath our lives,
one that sucked up the light
and created darkness
where the light might have been.
But we never got it.
We believed

with all our thumping little hearts
that something was terrible and impor
and probably our job to fix
if we could just figure out
what in the big wide world
it was.

Three by...

Susan Berlin
Mistress

He uses her sparingly
between his divorces, as
Europeans use sorbet,
to cleanse the palate
between courses.

Hippocrates Redux

Doctors always
wear soft-soled shoes,
cushioning the messenger,
if not the news.

Qualifier

It's *February*, sir,
that's the cruelest month,
once your days
are numbered.

Pamela Ethington
Suburban Life

I would write a poem about my childhood
but if you're going to write poetry
you need to use words like "bitter" or "soul dead" or
something that expresses some sort of
angst

and all I can think of is my mother's tuna casserole
with the peas and Campbell's cream of mushroom soup and those
chow mein noodles that were so popular in the 50s
the kind we would eat as a snack right out of the can
if we could get them before she turned them into that
tuna casserole

and about the most dangerous thing in our lives was just
when she would pull out the pack of
True cigarettes she kept in the freezer
light one up and cry and sometimes
drive off in the car after finishing it

I got scared when I smelled those cigarettes

I was never really sure if it was us or the casseroles
or the ranch house we lived in or just what
bitter soul-dead thing had come to roost in her
spreading its shadow
over all of us

Bobbi Dykema Katsanis
Incarnation

It is not just an exquisite fruitful longing
nor only a body, framed in a crimson mandorla
capitulating toward heaven.
Many a diurnal beast's
gone slouching toward a place configured holy,
face smeared with starlight.
It is not even the agony of the wicked;
but the place where the little chickens
gather meal from among the gritty dust.
We are. It is an off-tempo mood,
toes tapping irritatedly at the overextended wait.
A hill crowned with a childlike carpentry;
the idleness of hours; a pair of glassy, flyblown eyes.
Hope springing from the blackly bubbling swamp
in the shape of a new-hatched tadpole.
The sun feathering its wings,
o Icarus, amazing to see such heights,
so labyrinthine are the leagues of man.
The lightness in the step of the young woman
who goes out to her chores singing,
and the individual held note
in every choir, of the deepest basso profundo.
The resonance of oaken-timbered stalls
in shadowed, magisterial cathedrals.
It is the sunset overlooked with a lover
too intent on kissing,
the embrace of the patient ancestor at fireside,
a close-clipped camel's champing at the meager grass,
turning solidly down the road toward home.

Incarnation first appeared in Ginosko #4, www.ginoskoliteraryjournal.com.

New Husband, Home for Christmas

On television, a cheetah takes down a gazelle,
komodo dragons greedily demolish goats,
Technicolor fish dart through otherworldly reefs.

But here,
driving north on gravel in South Dakota,
frost shimmers thickly on bare trees.
Not twenty yards from the road,
six deer scamper through the frozen scrub,
coats tawny, winter plush,
breath alive and white;
twenty more stand restless in a draw.

My husband, city-bred,
is as enchanted as a child,
with nothing to compare it to
but television.

But I grew up among coyote,
white-tails, mule deer, ground squirrels,
meadowlarks, golden hawk, and badger.

I envy him this newness.
He envies my familiarity—
the magi bring their gifts.

Alinda Wasner

Heaven, she supposes...

is that place where the cops
do not leave the ladder
leaning against the house
for three days, the alarm
blaring so the whole damn world
knows you've been gone
for at least a week—
where they at least scoop up the dead rat
outside McDonald's
or the tennis shoes
from of the middle of Jefferson Avenue
where the child got hit
instead of leaving them
there like some sort of admonition;

heaven, she supposes
is where the thief
who gets in at night even if you are home
does it discreetly,
almost Biblically,
stealing only the important things
in such a way
that you think
you've merely misplaced them—
the earrings in a pocket maybe
or the wedding ring
on the back of the sink
instead of tearing the place apart
ransacking even the children's room
as if they own stock in Fisher-Price
and hide it in the Play Family Village;

heaven, she supposes
might even have been that place
on Lenox Street
where the curtains were yellow

and the cutlery matched
if only her Mama'd taken her
in her arms
and said, O Baby
why didn't you tell me?
instead of smacking her
until her eyes swelled shut
as if not being able to see the man
she made her call Daddy
sneak into her room
at night
would mean it didn't happen.

O God, she thinks,
somewhere in the desert
there must be a cold stream
where you can lie down
and let the water turn the blood
to ice in your veins—
let you be sucked under
just long enough
so that when you come up
(if you come up—if you have to)
it is someplace downstream
where, even if it is the Detroit Riv
at least you'll be numb enough
so that when
you catch your reflection
you won't be totally mystified
if it shifts
and everything seems
entirely different.

Heaven She Supposes first appeared
in Comstock Review 2008.

And so you...

put on the red mini dress
and you tell the sitter
that you'll be back
before ten
because you're still breast feeding
and even though it's the Winans
and the tickets were pricey
and you should stay the whole time
you won't even though you'll be tempted
because at some point during *Celebrate New Life*
there is this feeling of dread
that even if you come home earlier
than you said
she'll be asleep on the sofa
and the baby will have
cried so long
that the three-year old
will try to feed him
and there will be
a busted jar of Gerber's
on the floor by the fireplace
there will be glass in their hands
and in the baby's diaper
and blood
will be everywhere
and your fingers will be
shaking so bad
you can't dial the doctor
all you'll be able to do
is scream at her lazy ass
threaten to slit her throat
except that
the children are waiting
for you to
catch them up
bury your face
in their shirts,
breathe the life
their very souls
back into them.

Doris Ivie
Three Haiku

Mending Rifts

Mending rifts takes time
Even lacewings can rebuild
Given thread and light

Crossing Sixty

Flow into this age
all rocky, ragged and raw
on hawk wings, ready

Ever Present Ants

Ever present ants
scuttling dead leaves with heart
no need for shovels

Ellen LaFlèche

Gulsum, a 16-year-old Afghani Girl, Sets Herself
On Fire After Being Beaten by Her Husband

Gulsum pours lamp oil over her head,
lets the warm liquid rain-soak into her roots.

She strokes the match. Flames
finger-crawl up Gulsum's arm.
Her hair flares. Black curls
burn to crackle and smoke.

Her husband turns.

A neighbor woman beats the blaze
with her veil. It is her best veil—
white silk, red-embroidered with roses.
The veil vaporizes.

The scent of scorched rose petals
lingers in the ambulance.

Only later
in the sterile burn unit
does Gulsum smell the burned half of her face,
the soot like vacuum dust in her lungs.

The nurse dribbles apricot juice
on Gulsum's tongue. Her lips sip the nectar.
The sweetness lingers kiss-sticky in her mouth.

When the doctor unwinds—slow as love—
the white shroud from her head
Gulsum watches in the hand mirror.
The unveiling reveals the tired,
half-turned face of an old midwife.

Gulsum looks at her good right eye:
black-lashed, it is pretty enough
for flirting with the doctor. Its iris
blooms big with morphine.

The midwife's eye cries.
The teenager's eye dreams the future.

The Parish Housekeeper Cleans the Church
After the Funeral of a Young Soldier Killed in Iraq

Bertha smells the post-dirge darkness,
the sad candles swaying in tiered
rows like a chorus of mourners.

In the front pew she finds a tranquilizer.
It is white as a de-nucleated eye.
Bertha stares into its blankness
then swallows it down.

On her knees she sweeps up grief's debris:
crumpled prayer cards, balled-up kleenex.
Dead carnation heads roll into her dustpan.

When Bertha plunges her mop into the wash bucket
its dreadlocks drip water like a baptized skull.

There are scuff marks to clean:
the soldier's widow drilled her black
high heels into the floor's pine planks.

Bertha still has the black dress,
the black purse from when her son
came home from Nam in a zippered bag.
She bought him a mahogany coffin
with glimmering brass handles.

Bertha scrubs the stations-of-the-cross:
that death story, sculpted out of the cold
stone wall. She touches the nail-heads,
the hole in his side.

Bertha washes his limbs, the limp
soles of his feet. She lingers in front of the tomb.
He sleeps, he sleeps so hard.

Christina Lovin
Never Tell

'What's past is nothing and remembering
is not seeing.
— **Fernando Pessoa,**
(as Alberto Ceiro)

Never tell what might have been—
dull stories of almost but not quite
and never was and who cares anyway
but fools babbling on of the heart
attack survived, the rabid dog outrun,
that turn at the last second—accident
that almost was, but wasn't—love
un-snared, so how can it be lost?

Move your hand across the bruised
limbs and knotted branches of grafted
apple trees, thick with spring and
        mourning
of the homeless swarm. Listen
to the high keening of the wind,
of widows—their voices sound the same
in winter—and learn that fruitless melody.
Taste the sea and someone else's tears
to understand your own are bland,
indistinct. New grass forgets
the sharp teeth of frost. Last summer
owns no light; it has been spent
among the high branches of the pines.

Crickets' cadenced dirges, whirring
downward of maple seeds to their own
burial, death rattles in the narrow throat
of the desiccated gourd: herein
lay a hundred million secrets,
but only one revelation, one
certainty—no matter what
might have been, what was.

Remember the trap you set as a child
just to see what could be caught—
crushed wing and broken leg
of the sparrow there, pale flesh
around the surprised round eyes—
how the sun shone down on you
both and on the winter lawn.

Never Tell first appeared in
What We Burned for Warmth,
Finishing Line Press (2006).

192

Bernard Mann
Sunsets

Moored, unhappily, on the east-facing slope,
he grumbled endlessly over sunset deprivation,
how the house afforded no vista of the clashing clouds,
the titanic spills of mauve and gold,
that others see.

Now and then he'd remember
to run errands around the time of day
when the sun went down,
nudging and tweaking the hour spent
to get him to the spicewood road
that ambled steeply down
the long west face of the hill that led
to the main road back,
and took his time, at that, raising tempers
in the cars behind him so that he would
descend the ridge to the beat
of the sun's own departing song.

He missed the Merrimack, where his home
had perched on the river's edge,
and bends on east and west caught the sun's
chromatic crescendos at first as it rose
and then as it set.

And glorious displays on Cape Cod's soughing shore,
and other lands' ends.

But now he grew older with every night's hello,
longing for the celestial furnace
that once kept him younger with every day's goodbye

.

Alice Owens Johnson
Writing Under the Gun

Summer brings rain and revolution.

Heat ripples down the cobbled streets
of Oaxaca, Oaxaca, the sing-song city
of heavy *cantera* stone. Quiet settles
during siesta, but at night the air clangs
with bells and the piercing *frisson* of bullets, sirens.

Echoing pings from the tortilla man's high-pitched
metal triangle says *safety in the street,* at least for the
moment. Indoors, my computer's cursor blinks at me
like the Cheshire cat. My mind is a split screen; one side
back flips with the image of a machete-wielding rebel, on the other
side my novel curls in sunlight, languorous as a napping kitten.

Each day I greet my novel,
I pray for a visitation. My Muse is Mexican;
she doesn't show up on time, sometimes not at all.
I want my characters to save me; pull me into the story so deeply
I can ignore the chaos and shattering light.
I sluice myself with Pound's raspy advice: "Make it new, make it new."

In the *Jacaranda* tree, boughs sag with bright green birds. They caw
Make it weird, make it strange. Just make it.
I bargain, burn *copal* all summer. I beg for a cloak
of words to muffle the exploding story outside my window.

At last she comes. In the middle of that quiet moment
soft as rustling corn sheaves, I know the story
in the character, the character in the story. I enter Camille's
mind and body. My sweet, lost child reveals
herself. I know why her heart churns and spits.
I finally know her secret. I pick up my pen and write.

Cynthia West
Where We Did Not Love

In the evening quiet
    the Moonlight Sonata sounds, my mother
    playing her aloneness on notes
    of gathering dark. Her inability to teach
    me how to touch
    rings in every fading chord,
    defining the separate grief of night.
The heavy-shadowed house refuses to leave
    my dusty mind. No amount of washing
    dissolves this photo printed with lonely ink.

My bedroom is here, where we did not love.
The swing-set rusts by the garden shed.
If I could repair it, could I bring you,
    my own children, from the distant cities
    where I taught you to live? Could I find you
    where you hide in law-suits, addiction, debt?
Could I dare to break the old pattern
    that I passed along?

Let me kneel down before you, touch you
    with all the bluebells we never had the time
    to notice. Let us finally inhabit the rooms
    that have waited empty
    for our tears. When we open the windows
    the sad music will bloom.

Ronda Broatch
Two Loaves

Our rooms are infused with the scent
of bread—two loaves,
one plain,

one dotted with millet, quinoa, wheat
germ—a reflection of my need
to complicate the simple.

My daughter kneads
just so long, palm to sticky
dough to which she adds

a hint of flour. My own
clay beats the walls of the mixing bowl,
a testament to tired hands,

less time. Our mounds rise
and we push them down with the heels
of our hands, fold them

into fat origami flowers, cup them
taut as a ball,
firm belly dough.

I watch her turn
her round on the counter,
some magic maneuver she learned

from another. Our loaves
ascend again in clay pans
and what I've let go these past years

returns, if briefly. In the oven our breads
expand over steaming water,
crusts form hard and dark,

hers smooth, mine scarred on top
and spreading open. Our two loaves
cool on racks, *still baking inside*

she tells me, before the knife
releases heat and the scent of
what is possible in time.

He calls to her and she ascends...

step by wooden step
to the bedroom where he lies
on a horse hair mattress deepened
with forty years.
She straightens his tangled sheets,

listens as he tries again to rouse
the sleeping soldier on the bus.
It is 1941; he knows they are nearly home.
It is the year after coming to America,
after the camps, a book mostly written.
Sometimes

he still reaches trembling fingers
to conceal the window shrapnel sliced
into a brother's skull.
Germany, front line, 1915.
She catches his hand, gives him
water and something for sleep.
Sometimes
he doesn't
know her.
She looks beyond the curtain

to the tree he grafted,
tiny limb wrapped firmly until it held.
She knows its broad sweep, apples,
seedless, green.
She'll stoop to collect them in a paper sack,
later when they fall.

Michael Sweeney
Holy Icons of Mother Russia

for Patricia Elizabeth Sweeney

Christ himself allowed Saint Luke to paint his sacred portrait
so there's no idolatry, just honest craftsmanship, icons on wood
a thousand years old hacked from deserving trees, wood that
serfs might've gladly burned mounted for public display, hung
for agnostics & worse, every heart-shaped countenance utterly
disengaged. You can stand with them like Pasternak & not be
the wiser man, not till you face your shame, flog an already
broken horse or beg for your worthless life but witness that dread
ascent, however you kneel or crawl. How can they float above
altar & cross on solar vermilion rays? How can that primitive
blood-orange light seep from their flaking pores? How can they
breathe those turquoise hues without getting vertigo? They're
not human, those martyrs & saints, those translucent Roswell
eyes, they see Chernobyl & Babi Yar, the gulags you resurrect
no matter your tongue or creed. An innocent system & a guilty
defendant, that's what John Ashcroft said, you can believe
Raskolnikov opened his wretched heart. You can look through
them like cold stained glass warmed by the Arctic sun, where
suffering's sacrosanct. You can appreciate anything
executed so well

David Witherspoon
Silly Geese

What the field guide calls "rich, musical honking" makes
me look up from my yard work for the V-shaped flock
winging north, but only four appear, the wild pibroch
resounding in their litany of desire that awakes
space rendering sky a cupola. The mind forsakes
its small talk, the cove is a temple. Like some ad hoc
steering committee they argue all morning, as if in shock
at losing the way, up and down the river in a file that takes
them nowhere. He who ardently honks with every wing beat
wants to head straight for Baffin Island, but the leader says we
are nearing the mountains of Carolina, where streams flow sweet
and air is cool enough without flying thousands of miles just to be
like every other goose. Or maybe they simply discuss where to eat
next. I myself will stay here, birds and seasons flowing through me.

Laura Still
Forgotten Language

> *Once I spoke the language of flowers—*
> *How did it go?*
> *How did it go?* —Shel Silverstein

Soft summer grass murmuring tenderness against my cheek,
sweet smack of buttercup kisses
grasshoppers prattling in buzzy whirs and clicks,
lazy dandelion hours watching shade stretch over ground,
gone
silent as light leaves treetops, sudden as a last kiss.

When did I stop attending
the blossom of morning glories under my window,
their drowsy buttoning up at twilight?
Did the wild violets grow mute, lilies cease their fanfare?
I need to soak my skin in moonlight, stare a few hours
at stars, leave myself out in the rain, lay my ear
against hollow earth, sing till music echoes back,
dance till my feet stop hurting—blunder, laugh,
bruise my way through—
till I fall into the river of words forgotten
and it drowns me with remembering.

Anthony Hughes
Bliss

On the bank under the green spring willow,
he loves a woman with his eyes.

She gathers up her dress, just above the knee,
and steps into the incandescent stream.

The white water curtsies round her ankles.
Tonight, the moon will set in the small of her back.

Nellie Hill
City Slickers

How mean it was of him to bring the deer to the house
when he knew it was for her but pretended
to be giving it to both of them;
and like a buddy showed the husband
how to carve the fur and skin from the fat
and the fat from the meat and how to separate
the muscles and tendons and how to go around
the genitals and the anus and how to pull the guts out
and the liver and the heart and how to do the job.

He enjoyed telling the husband what to do
as if he were telling him how to make love to her,
but the husband thought it was about the deer
and the knife and the body and their meal.

And she saw this and thought it funny
because the lovemaking she had with the hunter
was simple, like something alive,
an engine with its own heart that might,
at any moment, run away.

The Word

Make it my name you say and mine you hear
in your sleep my ears near your mouth my arms
in your arms and your hands wrapped in mine
for this one late moment before we turn aside
as earth opens up and swallows us
our complaints and yearnings our harsh syllables
our mouths empty of names and no skull
to fill the hollows of our hands or shore to follow
barefoot behind the summer flies. Take this image
into the center of your hand and fold it
into mine as if into a canvas the landscape of
thought desire winter summer all extremes until
we've swallowed the word and the world
of words the world the last

After Camus' Story, 'The Adulterous Wife'

She went into the hall
down the stairs, left him
in their bed breathing the heaving
rhythms of sleep. He turned
and groaned

as she walked though the rooms to the stairs,
and the front door and walked out
into the coolness, the garlands of stars
and the dark sky beyond.
She walked along wet grass into the forested
hillside, overlooking the neighbors
with their midnight lights and dogs;
and she watched the shadows carefully
and heard the whispers of men from ways
still foreign to her as she moved
through the tall grasses, thinking of love,
gliding to the calls of foxes, and the sounds
of deer tumbling into the orchard.

Donna Naney
Nature's Children

Mountain lions lurked in those hills,
rattlesnakes plentiful
in the playland of my childhood.

With loud determined innocence,
we stomped our territory,
marked our terrain.
What predator would dare cross the line?

Flying down the dry yellow grass of summer
on flattened cardboard—
magic carpets carried us
invincible
over irresistible hills.

Our joyful play so profound
I dream about it to this day.
We owned those hills
in the hot dry summers
of our intrepid souls

~ Notes On Contributors ~

Jacob Appel, winner of the *NMW* Fiction Award, has a master's from New York University and the Harvard Law School. His work has appeared widely, and he has been short-listed for the O. Henry Award and the Pushcart Prize. He's won the *NMW* Fiction Prize twice previously. He teaches bioethics and is researching pediatric euthanasia and elective limb amputation. Visit www.jacobmappel.com.

Louise Aronson, winner of the *NMW* Short-Short Fiction Award, has a master's from Warren Wilson College, and is a practicing physician at UC, San Francisco. 'After,' herein, is her first 'literary publication.'

Harry Bauld, winner of the *NMW* Poetry Award, grew up in Medford, MA, and was educated at Columbia. He is a former All-Ivy shortstop, "drinks columnist" for *Boston Magazine* and a "Vermont prep-school boxing coach." Now he teaches in New York. Poems have appeared or are forthcoming in *The Southeast Review, The Litchfield Review, Deliberately Thirsty* (UK), *Whiskey Island, Elysian Fields Quarterly* and others.

M. Garrett Bauman, winner of the *NMW* Nonfiction Award, was raised in the inner city of Paterson, NJ, but "lives one mile from the nearest road in rural New York." He has published in *Sierra, The New York Times* and literary magazines.

Susan Berlin lives in Massachusetts. Her poems have appeared in the *Harvard Review, Ploughshares* and many other literary venues. Twice a finalist in the National Poetry Series, six-time nominee for a Pushcart Prize, she was awarded the 16th Annual Galway Kinnell Poetry Prize and recently received an International Publication Prize from the *Atlanta Review* for Outstanding Poetic Achievement.

Ronda Broatch is the author of *Shedding Our Skins* (Finishing Line Press, 2008) and *Some Other Eden* (FLP, 2005). Nominated for the Pushcart Prize and Best of the Web, Ronda is the recipient of the 2007 Artist Trust GAP Grant.

Eve Brown lives in Western Massachusetts and has traveled widely. Her fish-out-of-water travel memoir, *Take Me Home: My Search for Meaning—and a decent restroom—in the Third World* (Random House) will be published in Spring of 2009.

Patrick Carrington is the author of *Hard Blessings* (MSR Publishing, 2008), *Thirst* (Codhill, 2007), *Rise, Fall and Acceptance* (MSR Publishing, 2006); winner of *New Delta Review's* 2008 Matt Clark Prize and *Yemassee's* Pocataligo Poetry Prize. New poems are in *West Branch, National Poetry Review, Bellingham Review, American Literary Review, Bellevue Literary Review* and elsewhere. He teaches writing in New Jersey and is poetry editor of *Mannequin Envy* (www.mannequinenvy.com).

Katherine Case (MFA, Mills College) is a poet, letterpress printer for Thicket Press and former Peace Corps volunteer. Awards include the Mary Merritt Prize for Poetry and Ardella Mills Essay Prize. Poetry has appeared in *Gastronomica, Squaw Valley Review, Parthenon West, Cicada* and *Oklahoma Review.* She was a finalist for the 2002 Emily Dickinson Award and the 2005 Pablo Neruda Poetry Prize.

Susan Chiavelli, winner of the *NMW* Short-Short Fiction Award, is a native of Seattle and lives in Santa Barbara. Awards include the 2008 Lamar York Nonfiction Prize from *Chattahoochee Review*. Stories have won prizes from *Minnetonka Review and 580 Split* and have appeared in *Other Voices, Spindrift, Lunch Hour Stories,* and on stage at *Speaking of Stories.*

Mary Cole is an artist and poet living on Cape Ann, MA. Poems have appeared in *Portrait of the Artist as Poet* (Magnolia St. Publishers), an anthology edited by Carol Thayer Cox and Peggy Osna Heller

Sarah Coury attends Western Michigan University, pursuing a degree in creative

writing and photography. She lives in Marshall, MI, with her husband and son.
Ruth Daigon was founder and editor of *Poets On:* for 20 years until it ceased
publication. Poems have appeared in many media. Awards include The Ann Stanford
Prize and the Greensboro Poetry Award. The latest of seven books is *Payday At The
Triangle* (Small Poetry Press) based on the Triangle Shirtwaist Factory Fire in 1911.
Handfuls of Time was published in 2002. She is featured in *Modern American Poets
in English and Thai,* a product of an exchange program. Garrison Keillor has featured
her poetry on public radio.

Barbara de la Cuesta has lived in Colombia and Venezuela. She teaches English as
a Second Language at the Ocean County College. Her novel, *The Gold Mine,* was
published in 1988 (Latin American Literary Review) and *The Spanish Teacher* in
2007 (Gival Press). Poems have appeared in *California Quarterly, Texas Review* and
elsewhere. Awards include fellowships from the Massachusetts Artists Foundation,
New Jersey Council on the Arts and the Geraldine Dodge fellowship.

Vicki Goodfellow Duke lives in Calgary, Alberta, CAN, where she teaches Oral
Interpretation of Literature at Mount Royal College. Awards include the Dorothy
Sargent Rosenberg Poetry Prize, the Ray Burrell Award and the Friends Prize. Poems
have appeared in *Kaleidowhirl, Rock Salt Plum Poetry Review, Room of One's Own*
and *Circle Magazine.*

Pamela Ethington is a writer and editorial assistant at Le Moyne College in
Syracuse, NY.

Merle Feld is the author of *A Spiritual Life: Exploring the Heart and Jewish
Tradition* (State University of New York Press, revised 2007), a memoir in poetry and
prose, and the award-winning plays, *The Gates are Closing* and *Across the Jordan,*
included in the anthology *Making a Scene* (Syracuse University Press, 1997). She is
Founding Director of the Rabbinic Writing Institute.

Britton Gildersleeve, winner of the *NMW* Nonfiction Award, teaches at Oklahoma
State University, where she directs the OSU Writing Project, a non-profit for teachers.
"During her commute from Tulsa, she dreams of returning to Southeast Asia and
writing the great American essay cycle."

Diane Gilliam grew up in Columbus, OH. Awards include the 2008 Chaffin Award
for Appalachian Literature, 2003 Ohio Arts Council Fellowship, the 2005 Ohioana
Library Association Book of the Year Award in Poetry for *Kettle Bottom,* which also
won a Pushcart and an American Booksellers Association Book Sense Pick for the
Top Ten Poetry Books of 2005. Other books include *One of Everything* and *Recipe
for Blackberry Cake* (chapbook).

Jenny Gumpertz "came to writing after having already had careers in showbiz and
nonfiction editing." 'Peeling Onions,' herein, is her first fiction in a book. She recently
won an award in a Jane's Stories Press contest, and was published online.

Gayle Elen Harvey has had work in *The New York Quarterly, So To Speak, Visions
International* and *Poetry Northwest.* She's won top prizes from NYS Foundation for
the Arts, *Ekphrasis, Columbia Arts & Letters, Frances Locke/The Bitter Oleander*
and *Sow's Ear* poetry chapbook competition. "Eating barracuda and petting a Catskill
Mountains rattlesnake helped prepare me for the poet's life."

Nellie Hill's poetry and stories have appeared in *Harvard Magazine, Poetry East,
American Poetry Review, Alaska Quarterly* and elsewhere, including three
chapbooks, *Astrolabes, Having Come This Far* and *Geographies.* She has a private
acupressure practice in Berkeley.

Laura Hilton, Auburn, CA, "was catapulted into writing some eighteen months ago." Favorite quote—Whitman: "Walt, you contain enough, why don't you let it out then?" Her poems have appeared in *Freefall, Ship of Fools* and *Tiger's Eye*.

Gindy Elizabeth Houston "began writing at age 23 in September of 2001...." One day she "decided to take a chance and wrote to Maxine Kumin," who put her in touch with Cecilia Woloch, who became a friend and mentor and tough critic.

Dr. Anthony Hughes holds a doctorate from SUNY. Works have appeared widely. He is an English Professor at Hilbert College in Hamburg, NY, where he teaches writing, film, literature, poetry and Romanticism. He lives in Orchard Park "with two dogs and a cat and a salt-water aquarium with a sea rose anemone about the size of a dinner plate."

David Hunter is a decorated former police officer, a 20-year editorial columnist for the *Knoxville News-Sentinel,* author of 15 books—novels, memoirs and true crime—and a contributing editor to *NMW*. Awards include the Knoxville Writers' Guild 2008 Career Achievement Award. He was nominated for an Edgar for his first mystery novel, *The Jigsaw Man,* and the Appalachian Writers Best Book Award for *The Archangel Caper*. His work has appeared in *Mad, Reader's Digest* and elsewhere. His latest novel is *Tempest at the Sunsphere,* first in a series set in Knoxville, where he lives with his wife, Cheryl.

Stephen Irwin, winner of the *NMW* Fiction Award, has been honored in Australia and elsewhere for short films he's written and directed. Poems have appeared in the prestigious Newcastle Poetry anthologies. He is the first non-American to win a first-place award from *NMW*.

Doris Ivie, a contributing poetry editor for *NMW*, is a Knoxville poet, essayist and Professor Emeritus "basking in the freedom of her sixth decade," exploring shamanic healing, string theory, live music, international travel, and "the wonder of each moment."

Alice Owens Johnson penned "Writing Under the Gun" during the revolution in Oaxaca, MEX. Works have appeared widely, including the *O. Henry Festival of Short Stories, I Thought My Father was God*, edited by Paul Auster, and *Alice Redux: Tales of Alice in Wonderland and Lewis Carroll*. Awards include finalist in the Hidden River Arts Awards, *2007*. She recently completed a novel about New Orleans in the turbulent 1950's. "New Orleans is my home no matter where I live," which includes Black Mountain, N.C.

Angela Masterson Jones is a copy editor who serves on the Advisory Board of Spoonbill Cove Press and published her first poetry collection, *Broken Kisses*, in 2004. Prize-winning poetry and prose have appeared in *Writer's Digest, St. Petersburg Times, American Poetry Anthology, Sabal, Penumbra, Sunscripts* and elsewhere. She studies writing at Eckerd College in St. Petersburg, FL.

Bobbi Dykema Katsanis is pursuing her doctorate in Art and Religion at the Graduate Theological Union, Berkeley. Works have appeared in *Sacred Journey, The Litchfield Review, Ruah*, and *The Binnacle*.

Pat Landreth Keller's awards include a poetry prize from the Georgia Council for the Arts, the 2008 Southeast Missouri State University Press short fiction award for "The Magician's Assistant," published in the Spring issue of *Big Muddy: A Journal of the Mississippi River Valley*. A poetry chapbook, *Draglines*, was selected for the 2008 Toadlily Press Quartet series.

Cathy Kodra lives in Knoxville with her husband and two youngest children. Her works have appeared in *NMW, Tar Wolf Review, Birmingham Arts Journal, Main Channel Voices* and elsewhere. 'The Most Interesting Thing in the World,' herein, is her first published short story.

Ellen LaFlèche has worked as a journalist and women's health educator in western Massachusetts. Publications include *The Ledge,* and *Words and Pictures* magazine.

Wayne Lee has worked as a commercial fisherman in Alaska, an anodizing technician in CO, a waiter at the Space Needle in Seattle, a journalist for *The Seattle Times*, and the *Washington D.C. Times,* a fisheries marketing specialist in Indonesia and public information officer for five government agencies. He owns and operates Club Z! In-Home Tutoring Services of Santa Fe, NM. Poems have appeared widely, including *The Ledge, Poetry Motel, The Floating Bridge Press Anthology, Jones Av., California Quarterly, Writer's Digest, Sage Trail, New England Anthology of Poets, Thanatos, Exquisite Reaction, Jeopardy, Matrix* and *Vega.* Awards include the Emily Dickinson Award, the William Stafford Award, the Robert Penn Warren Award, the Charles Proctor Humor Award, *Writer's Digest* Writing Awards and the *Santa Fe Reporter's War and Peace* Poetry Contest. He is co-author, with his wife Alice Morse Lee, of *Twenty Poems from the Blue House.*

Christina Lovin is the author of *What We Burned for Warmth* and *Little Fires.* Her work is widely published and anthologized. Awards include artists' grants from the Kentucky Arts Council and the Kentucky Foundation for Women.

Bernard Mann lives in Austin, where he plans and designs environmental and architectural projects, engages in citizen activism to protect habitat and scenic resources, and writes poetry.

Rebekah McCarroll's works have appeared in *Downtown Knoxville, Everything West* and *Eva.* She has "experienced everything from Woodstock to Wall Street, martial arts to professional modeling, medical expertise to management, and the rigorous joys of motherhood. Life is good."

Don Mitchell lives in upstate New York. He is an anthropologist and has been a professor, ultra-marathoner, photographer, road-race timer, computer programmer, and renovator of old houses. His poetry, fiction, and photographs have appeared in *Humanistic Anthropology, Green Mountains Review, Discover* and elsewhere.

Karla K. Morton's work has appeared widely in Texas publications and elsewhere. Awards include finalist in the North Texas Book Festival. She loves to give talks and readings. Website: www.kkmorton.com.

Donna Naney has lived in California and Tennessee. Her heart "resides in both places." 'Nature's Children,' herein, is her first published poem.

Amy Nawrocki teaches English at the University of Bridgeport. She won the 2008 Writing Contest from *The Litchfield Review.* Her new book is *Potato Eaters,* Finishing Line Press (fall, 2008).

Angella M. Nazarian teaches psychology at universities in the Los Angeles area. She has great interest in Eastern mysticism and poetry.

Mil Norman-Risch, winner of the *NMW* Nonfiction Award, is the winner of *American Poetry Journal's* 2007 American Poet's Prize. Credits include *Willow Springs, White Pelican Review, Sojourners, Freshwater, Common Ground Review, Avatar Review* and Agha Shahid Ali's anthology, *Ravishing DisUnities* (Wesleyan University Press, 2001). She teaches and writes in Richmond, VA.

Suzanne Owens's work has appeared widely, including *Ploughshares,* which ran excerpts from her poetry cycle, *Ten Days In Russia.* Chapbooks include *Theater*

Poems (Frank Cat Press), *In The Lake's Eye*, *Harvesting Ice* (Finishing Line Press) and *Over the Edge* (Pudding House Press). Awards include the A. Poulin Jr. New Poets of America prize for her book, *The Daughters of Discordia* (BOA Edition).

Adrienne Pond, winner of the *NMW* Short-Short Fiction Award, has lived in several countries. "She is grateful to all who have risked something on her behalf."

Yvonne Postelle of San Rafael, CA, who favors formal verse, "has tried to write poetry since shortly after (she) learned to read."

Ralph Ryan, winner of the *NMW* Nonfiction Award, lives in Northern California in a mountaintop home he built with his "two sons and fiancee." He works for the City of Redding.

Charles Sharpe lives on Bainbridge Island, WA, and "writes poetry when not working as a construction superintendent. He sent a poem to his mother for her birthday a few years back, which she edited and sent back to him. Despite the misgivings of those closest to him, he soldiers on in a somewhat game fashion, and has appeared in several literary journals."

Mark Sieger has been a graphic designer and artist for thirty years. He lives in Knoxville with his wife, Lucy, and two dogs, Daisy and Jasper. He manages the graphic design department at Oak Ridge Associated Universities.

Laura Spagnoli's work has most recently appeared in *Philadelphia Stories*. She is an assistant professor of French at Temple University, where she founded and edits a literary magazine for world languages. Visit http://www.temple.edu/inotherwords.

Cornelia C. Stanton, poet, violinist, is pursuing an MFA at Bennington Writing Seminars. She was a finalist in the 2001 *Arts & Letters* poetry competition.

Kurt Steinwand's work has appeared in *Poet Lore, White Pelican Review* and other journals. Kurt is also an award-winning artist and graphic designer.

Laura Still, a contributing poetry editor for *NMW*, lives with her two sons in Knoxville, where she works as a dental hygienist, a USTA certified tennis umpire and in sales. She has screened novels for the Peter Taylor Prize on behalf of the Knoxville Writers Guild, which she also has served as treasurer and as director of the Young Writers Poetry Prize. She is a playwright and producer of children's plays for Church St. United Methodist Church. Poems have appeared in *New Millennium Writings, Knoxville Bound, Growing Up Girl*, and several KWG anthologies, including *Outscapes* (2008).

Ellen Sullins, winner of the *NMW* Poetry Award, was raised on a farm in Missouri, but now lives in Tucson, AZ. She has a doctorate in social psychology and for 15 years was a university teacher and researcher. She divides her time between practicing psychotherapy and poetry. Credits include *Nimrod, South Carolina Review, descant, Concho River Review, Calyx, Red Wheelbarrow* and her chapbook, *Elsewhere,* (Plan B Press, 2007).

Michael Sweeney a two-time Pushcart Prize nominee, teaches at Fairfield University and is the author of *In Memory of the Fast Break*, forthcoming from Plain View Press. Awards include runner-up for in the St. Louis Poetry Center's *Strong Medicine* contest.

Emily Tallman has a master's from California State University, Fresno. She lives in Oakland, "where she spends her free time collecting rejection letters from her favorite literary journals."

Dianalee Velie is a graduate of Sarah Lawrence College, and has a master's in writing from Manhattanville College where she served as faculty advisor of *Inkwell: A Literary Magazine*. She has taught poetry, memoir, and short story throughout the Northeast. Her prizewinning prose and poetry have been widely published, including three books of poetry, *Glass House* by First Edition and *The Many Roads to Paradise* by Rock Village Publishing. Her play, *Mama Says*, was directed by Daniel Quinn in a staged reading in New York. She is active in raising money for playgrounds and literacy. Website: www.veliefamilycircle.org.

Asha Vose, winner of the *NMW* Fiction Award, was accepted into the Tin House Summer Writers Workshop 2008. She has a bachelor's from the University of Tennessee and has studied abroad at the University of Wales. Fiction has appeared in *Harpur Palate, Quiddity*, and on public radio. She's a regular contributor for *Eva* magazine under the name Sarah Scoonover. She's at work on a collection of stories, *The Miracle of Electricity*.

Jeanne Wagner's many awards include the 2004 Stevens Manuscript Prize for her book, *The Zen Piano-Mover*. Other books include *The Falling Woman* by Puddinghouse Press (2001), *The Conjurer* by Anabiosis (2004) and *Medusa in Therapy* from Poets Corner Press (2008).

Pamela Spiro Wagner is the co-author of *Divided Minds: Twin Sisters and Their Journey through Schizophrenia*, St Martin's Press. Other works include her new book, *We Mad Climb Shaky Ladders*, CavanKerry Press (2009). "The Prayers of the Mathematician," herein, won first place in the 2001-02 International Poetry Contest sponsored by the BBC World Service.

Alinda Wasner's work has appeared in thirty small press publications including *Fresh Water: Women Writing About the Great Lakes, Passages North, The Wayne Review, The Wittenberg Review* and *Michigan Natural Resources*. Awards include the Wayne State University Tompkins Prize, an Amelia Press Award, the Wittenberg Poetry Award, The Lester Crowell Creative Writing Award, The Judith Siegal Pearson Prize, a Mr. Cogito Press Award, a Flume Press Award, and a MacGuffin and many others. Chapbooks include, *Departures/Arrivals* by Ridgeway Press and *TailSpin*, from Erstwhile Press. She lives in Lansing, MI.

Don Williams, founding editor and publisher of *NMW*, is a magazine writer, short story writer and a columnist for Knoxville's only independent city newspaper, *Knoxville Voice*. He is also a blogger for *www.Knoxvoice.com*, and his political commentary appears widely, including *Media With Conscience (MWCnews.net), Opednews, Truthout, Commondreams, Buzzflash* and others. Awards include a Malcolm Law Journalism Prize, a Sigma Delta Chi Golden Presscard Award, an NEH Journalism Fellowship from the University of Michigan, first place awards from the Tennessee AP Managing Editors, Scripps Howard Newspapers and more. He is a founder of the Knoxville Writers Guild and the Leslie Garrett Award. His book, *Heroes, Sheroes and Zeroes, The Best Writings About People (NMW, 2005)* is due a second printing. He is finishing two novels set in Tennessee and Iraq.

David Witherspoon is a widely traveled musician and widely published writer. He is the author of two novels, *Callie* and *Easy Go* from Xlibris (2008). His new book of poetry is *Peasant Dance & Selected Poems*.

Barbara Zimmermann teaches fiction writing at Ball State University. Her fiction, creative nonfiction and poetry have appeared widely. She is the author of *James Lee Burke and the Soul of Dave Robicheaux*.